HEINEMANN MODULAR MATHEMATICS
for
EDEXCEL AS AND A-LEVEL

Revise for Pure Mathematics 2

Michael Kenwood

1 2 3 4 5 6 7 8 9

Heinemann

Edexcel
Success through qualifications

Heinemann Educational Publishers,
a division of Heinemann Publishers (Oxford) Ltd,
Halley Court, Jordan Hill, Oxford, OX2 8EJ

OXFORD MELBOURNE AUCKLAND JOHANNESBURG
BLANTYRE GABORONE PORTSMOUTH NH (USA) CHICAGO

First published 2001

05 04 03 02 01

10 9 8 7 6 5 4 3 2 1

ISBN 0 435 51111 4

Cover design by Gecko Limited

Original design by Geoffrey Wadsley; additional design work by Jim Turner

Typeset and illustrated by Tech-Set Limited, Gateshead, Tyne and Wear

Printed in Great Britain by Scotprint, Haddington

Acknowledgements:

The author wishes to thank Geoff Mannall for all his care, patience and generous help in reading the proofs, making many useful suggestions and checking the answers.

About this book

This book is designed to help you get your best possible grade in your Pure Mathematics 2 examination. The author is a former Principal Examiner and has a good understanding of Edexcel's requirements.

Revise for Pure Mathematics 2 covers the key topics that are tested in the Pure Mathematics 2 exam paper. You can use this book to help you revise at the end of your course, or you can use it throughout your course alongside the course textbook, *Heinemann Modular Mathematics for Edexcel AS and A-level Pure Mathematics 2*, which provides complete coverage of the syllabus.

Helping you prepare for your exam

To help you prepare, each topic offers you:

- **Key points to remember** – summarise the mathematical ideas you need to know and be able to use.
- **Worked examples and examination questions** – help you understand and remember important methods, and show you how to set out your answers clearly.
- **Revision exercises** – help you practise using these important methods to solve problems. Exam-level questions are included so you can be sure you are reaching the right standard, and answers are given at the back of the book so you can assess your progress.
- **Test yourself questions** – help you see where you need extra revision and practice. If you do need extra help they show you where to look in the *Heinemann Modular Mathematics for Edexcel AS and A-level Pure Mathematics 2* textbook.

Exam practice and advice on revising

Examination style paper – this paper at the end of the book provides a set of questions of examination standard. It gives you an opportunity to practise taking a complete exam before you meet the real thing. The answers are given at the back of the book.

How to revise – for advice on revising before the exam, read the **How to revise** section on the next page.

How to revise using this book

Making the best use of your revision time

The topics in this book have been arranged in a logical sequence so you can work your way through them from beginning to end. But **how** you work on them depends on how much time there is between now and your examination.

If you have plenty of time before the exam then you can **work through each topic in turn**, covering the key points and worked examples before doing the revision exercises and Test yourself questions.

If you are short of time then you can **work through the Test yourself sections first**, to help you see which topics you need to do further work on.

However much time you have to revise, make sure you break your revision into short blocks of about 40 minutes, separated by five- or ten-minute breaks. Nobody can study effectively for hours without a break.

Using the Test yourself sections

Each Test yourself section provides a set of key questions. Try each question:

- If you can do it and get the correct answer then move on to the next topic. Come back to this topic later to consolidate your knowledge and understanding by working through the key points, worked examples and revision exercises.
- If you cannot do the question, or get an incorrect answer or part answer, then work through the key points, worked examples and revision exercises before trying the Test yourself questions again. If you need more help, the cross-references beside each Test yourself question show you where to find relevant information in the *Heinemann Modular Mathematics for Edexcel AS and A-level Pure Mathematics 2* textbook.

Reviewing the key points

Most of the key points are straightforward ideas that you can learn: try to understand each one. Imagine explaining each idea to a friend in your own words, and say it out loud as you do so. This is a better way of making the ideas stick than just reading them silently from the page.

As you work through the book, remember to go back over key points from earlier topics at least once a week. This will help you to remember them in the exam.

Processing rational algebraic expressions

1

Key points to remember

1 To simplify a rational expression:

(i) factorize the numerator
(ii) factorize the denominator
(iii) cancel any factor common to both the numerator and denominator.

2 To add or subtract two algebraic fractions:

(i) put each fraction over a denominator equal to the lowest common multiple of the original two denominators
(ii) add or subtract
(iii) simplify as in **1**.

3 To multiply algebraic fractions:

(i) factorize the numerators
(ii) factorize the denominators
(iii) cancel each factor common to both a numerator and a denominator
(iv) multiply the terms remaining in the numerators
(v) multiply the terms remaining in the denominators.

4 To divide one algebraic fraction by another:

(i) turn the fraction after the division symbol upside down
(ii) change the division symbol to a multiplication symbol
(iii) proceed as in **3**.

Example 1

Simplify $\dfrac{4x^2-49}{2x^2-5x-42}$

Answer

$$\frac{4x^2-49}{2x^2-5x-42}$$

$$=\frac{(2x-7)(2x+7)}{(2x+7)(x-6)}$$ Using **1** (i) and (ii)

$$=\frac{2x-7}{x-6}$$ Using **1** (iii)

Example 2

Express $\dfrac{x+1}{2x-5}-\dfrac{x-2}{2x+1}$ as a single fraction in its lowest terms.

Answer

$$\frac{x+1}{2x-5}-\frac{x-2}{2x+1}$$

$$=\frac{(x+1)(2x+1)}{(2x-5)(2x+1)}-\frac{(x-2)(2x-5)}{(2x+1)(2x-5)}$$ Using **2** (i)

$$=\frac{2x^2+3x+1}{(2x-5)(2x+1)}-\frac{2x^2-9x+10}{(2x+1)(2x-5)}$$

$$=\frac{2x^2+3x+1-2x^2+9x-10}{(2x-5)(2x+1)}$$ Using **2** (ii)

$$=\frac{12x-9}{(2x-5)(2x+1)}$$ Simplifying

$$=\frac{3(4x-3)}{(2x-5)(2x+1)}$$

Example 3

Simplify $\dfrac{x^4-y^4}{x^2+xy}\div\dfrac{x^2+y^2}{x-y}$

Answer

$$\frac{x^4-y^4}{x^2+xy}\div\frac{x^2+y^2}{x-y}$$

$$=\frac{x^4-y^4}{x^2+xy}\times\frac{x-y}{x^2+y^2}$$ Using **4** (i) and (ii)

$$=\frac{(x^2-y^2)(x^2+y^2)}{x(x+y)}\times\frac{x-y}{x^2+y^2}$$ Using **3** (i) and (ii)

$$=\frac{(x-y)\cancel{(x+y)}\cancel{(x^2+y^2)}}{x\cancel{(x+y)}}\times\frac{x-y}{\cancel{x^2+y^2}}$$ Using **3** (i) and (iii)

$$=\frac{(x-y)^2}{x}$$

Example 4

Solve the equation

$$\frac{3x+1}{13x-3}+\frac{x}{x-1}=1$$

Answer

$$\frac{3x+1}{13x-3}+\frac{x}{x-1}=1$$

$$\frac{(3x+1)(x-1)}{(13x-3)(x-1)}+\frac{x(13x-3)}{(x-1)(13x-3)}=1$$ Using **2** (i)

$$\frac{3x^2-2x-1}{(13x-3)(x-1)}+\frac{13x^2-3x}{(x-1)(13x-3)}=1$$

$$\frac{3x^2-2x-1+13x^2-3x}{(x-1)(13x-3)}=1$$ Using **2** (ii)

$$\frac{16x^2-5x-1}{(x-1)(13x-3)}=1$$ Simplifying

$$16x^2-5x-1=(x-1)(13x-3)$$ Cross multiplying

$$16x^2-5x-1=13x^2-16x+3$$

$$3x^2+11x-4=0$$

$$(3x-1)(x+4)=0$$

$$x=\tfrac{1}{3} \text{ or } x=-4$$

Example 5

Find the value of x for which $\frac{1}{x}$, $\frac{1}{x+1}$ and $\frac{1}{x+4}$ are three consecutive terms of a geometric series.

Answer

Let $a=\frac{1}{x}$, $ar=\frac{1}{x+1}$

then $ar^2=\frac{1}{x+4}$

So $r=\dfrac{\frac{1}{x+1}}{\frac{1}{x}}$ and $r=\dfrac{\frac{1}{x+4}}{\frac{1}{x+1}}$ Using $\frac{ar}{a}=\frac{ar^2}{ar}=r$

$r=\frac{1}{x+1}\times\frac{x}{1}$ and $r=\frac{1}{x+4}\times\frac{x+1}{1}$ Using **4** (i) and (ii)

Hence $\frac{x}{x+1}=\frac{x+1}{x+4}$

$$x(x+4)=(x+1)(x+1)$$ Cross multiplying

$$x^2+4x=x^2+2x+1$$

$$2x-1=0$$

$$x=\tfrac{1}{2}$$

Revision exercise 1

1 Given that $\frac{1}{x} = \frac{2}{y} + \frac{3}{z}$, express z in terms of x and y.

In questions 2–8 simplify, giving your answer as a single fraction in its lowest terms.

2 $\frac{x^2 + 4x + 3}{x^2 - 1}$

3 $\frac{x^2 - 2x}{x^2 - 4} \times \frac{x^2 - 2x - 3}{x^2 - 3x}$

4 $\frac{6y^2 + 9y}{4y^2 - 9} \div \frac{12y^2}{2y^2 - y - 3}$

5 $\frac{1}{t} - \frac{2}{t+1} + \frac{1}{t+2}$

6 $\frac{2}{x^2 + 4x + 3} - \frac{1}{x^2 + 5x + 6}$

7 $\frac{2}{x^2 - x} - \frac{1}{x^2 + x} + \frac{3}{x}$

8 $\frac{2}{x - 1} - \frac{x + 1}{x(x - 1)} + \frac{1}{x + 1}$

In questions 9–12 find the values of x that satisfy the equation.

9 $\frac{1}{(x+2)^2} - \frac{1}{11x - 6} = 0$

10 $\frac{1}{x^2 - 1} = \frac{2}{3} - \frac{1}{x + 1}$

11 $\frac{x}{x + 1} - \frac{x - 1}{x} = \frac{1}{2}$

12 $\frac{x - 2}{x + 1} = 3 + \frac{2x + 1}{x - 1}$

13 Solve for x and y the simultaneous equations:

$$8x - 4y = 13$$

$$\frac{5}{x} + \frac{7}{y} = 6$$

14 By writing $t = \frac{x^2}{x + 1}$, find all the values of x for which

$$\frac{x^2}{x + 1} - \frac{x + 1}{x^2} = \frac{7}{12}$$

15 Find to 2 decimal places those values of x for which

$$\frac{3}{2x + 5} + \frac{1}{x - 1} = 1$$

Test yourself

What to review

If your answer is incorrect:

1 Simplify $\dfrac{(x^2+5x+6)(x+4)}{x^2-9}$

Review Heinemann Book P2 pages 1–10

2 Simplify $\dfrac{7}{(x-3)(x-4)} - \dfrac{4}{(x-1)(x-3)}$

Review Heinemann Book P2 pages 1–10

3 Simplify $\dfrac{2x^2+x-6}{2x^2-5x-25} \times \dfrac{5x^2-24x-5}{6x^2-x-12}$

Review Heinemann Book P2 pages 1–10

4 Simplify $\dfrac{6x^2+7x-3}{4x+x^2} \div \dfrac{4x^2-9}{5x^2+18x-8}$

Review Heinemann Book P2 pages 1–10

5 Find the value of x for which

$$\frac{1}{x-2} - \frac{1}{x-4} = \frac{1}{x-8} - \frac{1}{x-10}$$

Review Heinemann Book P2 pages 1–10

Test yourself answers

1 $\dfrac{x^2+6x+8}{x-3}$ **2** $\dfrac{3(x+3)}{(x-1)(x-3)(x-4)}$ **3** $\dfrac{5x^2+11x+2}{6x^2+23x+20}$ **4** $\dfrac{15x^2-11x+2}{x(2x-3)}$ **5** 6

Functions

2

Key points to remember

1 A function is a mapping between two variables, usually called x, the **independent** variable and y, the **dependent** variable.

2 The function f can be written as $\mathrm{f}: x \mapsto y$ or as $y = \mathrm{f}(x)$.

3 The set of values taken by x is called the **domain** of f and the corresponding set of values taken by y is called the **range** of f.

4 For two functions f and g, the composite function fg is obtained by applying g first, then f.

5 For a one–one function f the inverse function f^{-1} exists and

$$\mathrm{ff}^{-1}(x) = \mathrm{f}^{-1}\mathrm{f}(x) = x.$$

6 The graph of $y = \mathrm{f}^{-1}(x)$ is the reflection in the line $y = x$ of the graph of $y = \mathrm{f}(x)$.

7 The modulus function $|x|$ is defined:

$$|x| = x \quad \text{for } x \geqslant 0$$
$$|x| = -x \text{ for } x < 0.$$

8 To sketch the graph of $y = |\mathrm{f}(x)|$ from the graph of $y = \mathrm{f}(x)$:

(i) sketch $y = \mathrm{f}(x)$ for $\mathrm{f}(x)$ positive or zero
and (ii) sketch the reflection of $\mathrm{f}(x)$ in the x-axis for $\mathrm{f}(x)$ negative.

9 To sketch the graph of $y = \mathrm{f}(|x|)$ from the graph of $y = \mathrm{f}(x)$:

(i) sketch $y = \mathrm{f}(x)$ for x positive or zero
and (ii) reflect this in the y-axis to complete the sketch.

10 For any even function f,
$$f(x) = f(-x).$$

11 For any odd function f,
$$f(-x) = -f(x).$$

12 Transformations:
(i) $y = af(x)$: points on the x-axis remain unchanged and $[t, f(t)] \mapsto [t, af(t)]$
(ii) $y = f(x) + a$: translates in the y^+ direction for $a > 0$ and in the y^- direction for $a < 0$
(iii) $y = f(x + a)$: translates in the x^- direction for $a > 0$, and in the x^+ direction for $a < 0$
(iv) $y = f(ax)$: points on the y-axis remain unchanged and $[t, f(t)] \mapsto [t, f(at)]$.

13 To solve the equation $f(x) = g(x)$ graphically:
(i) draw the graphs of $y = f(x)$ and $y = g(x)$
(ii) the x-coordinates of their points of intersection are the solutions of the equation.

Example 1
The functions f and g are defined by

$$f: x \mapsto x^2 - 2, \qquad x \in \mathbb{R},$$
$$g: x \mapsto (x-2)^2, \qquad x \in \mathbb{R}.$$

Define in a similar way the functions ff, fg and gf.

Answer

Using **4**

$$\begin{aligned} ff(x) &= f[f(x)] \\ &= f(x^2 - 2) \\ &= (x^2 - 2)^2 - 2 \\ &= x^4 - 4x^2 + 4 - 2 \\ &= x^4 - 4x^2 + 2 \end{aligned}$$

So $ff: x \mapsto x^4 - 4x^2 + 2, \quad x \in \mathbb{R}$

Using **4**

$$\begin{aligned} fg(x) &= f[g(x)] \\ &= f[(x-2)^2] \\ &= [(x-2)^2]^2 - 2 \\ &= (x-2)^4 - 2 \\ &= x^4 - 8x^3 + 24x^2 - 32x + 16 - 2 \\ &= x^4 - 8x^3 + 24x^2 - 32x + 14 \end{aligned}$$

So $fg: x \mapsto x^4 - 8x^3 + 24x^2 - 32x + 14, \quad x \in \mathbb{R}$

$$\begin{aligned} gf(x) &= g[f(x)] \\ &= g[x^2 - 2] \\ &= [(x^2 - 2) - 2]^2 \\ &= (x^2 - 4)^2 \\ &= x^4 - 8x^2 + 16, \qquad x \in \mathbb{R} \end{aligned}$$

Using **4**

Example 2

Find the inverse function of

$$f: x \mapsto 3x - 4, \qquad x \in \mathbb{R}$$

Answer

Let $y = 3x - 4$

Using **5**

then $3x = y + 4$

$x = \frac{1}{3}(y + 4)$

Hence $f^{-1}: x \mapsto \frac{1}{3}(x + 4), \qquad x \in \mathbb{R}$

Example 3

The function f is defined by

$$f: x \mapsto \frac{2x - 1}{x + 3}, \qquad x \in \mathbb{R},\ x > -3$$

(a) Find the range of f.
(b) Find f^{-1} and state its domain.
(c) Sketch the curves with equations $y = f(x)$ and $y = f^{-1}(x)$.

Answer

(a) $f(-2) = -5,\ f(-1) = -\frac{3}{2},\ f(0) = -\frac{1}{3},\ f(1) = \frac{1}{4},\ f(2) = \frac{3}{5}, \ldots$

Also $\dfrac{2x - 1}{x + 3} = \dfrac{2 - \frac{1}{x}}{1 + \frac{3}{x}}$

As $x \to +\infty$, $\dfrac{1}{x} \to 0$ and $\dfrac{3}{x} \to 0$

So $\dfrac{2x - 1}{x + 3} \to 2$

The range of f is $y < 2$.

Using **3**

(b) Let $y = \dfrac{2x - 1}{x + 3}$

Using **5**

$$\begin{aligned} \text{Then } (x + 3)y &= 2x - 1 \\ xy + 3y &= 2x - 1 \\ 2x - xy &= 1 + 3y \\ x(2 - y) &= 1 + 3y \\ x &= \frac{1 + 3y}{2 - y} \end{aligned}$$

So $f^{-1}: x \mapsto \dfrac{1 + 3x}{2 - x}, \qquad x \in \mathbb{R},\ x < 2$ is the domain.

Using **3**

(c)

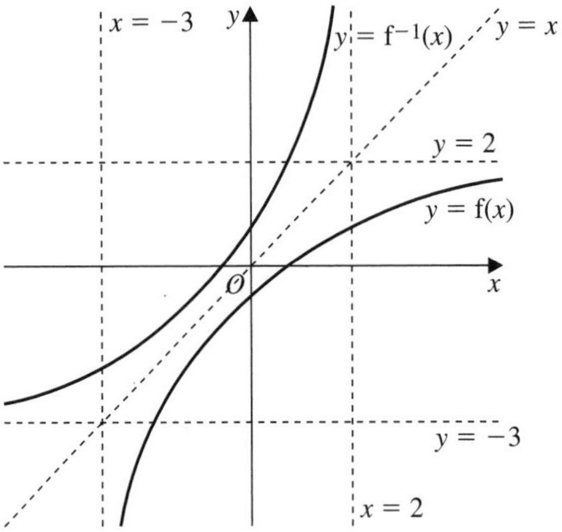

Using **6**

Example 4

A sketch of the curve with equation $y = \mathrm{f}(x)$ is shown.

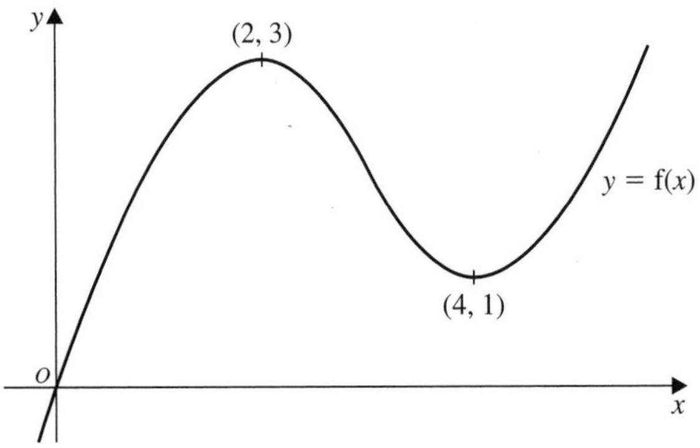

On separate diagrams, sketch the curves with equations:

(a) $y = \mathrm{f}(x + 2)$
(b) $y = 2\mathrm{f}(x)$
(c) $y = \mathrm{f}(2x)$

On each sketch mark the coordinates of the turning points and the x-coordinate of the point where the curve meets the x-axis.

Answer

(a)

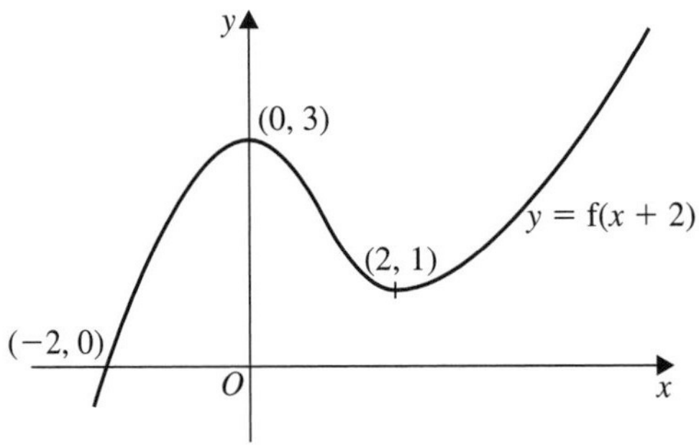

Using **12** (iii)

(b)

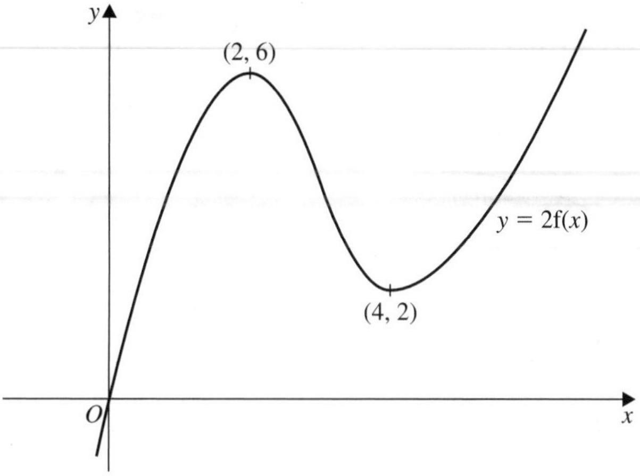

Using **12** (i)

(c)

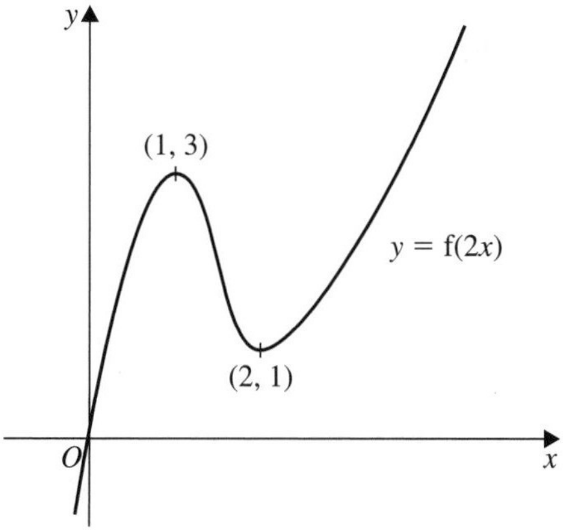

Using **12** (iv)

Example 5

f is an odd function such that

$$f(x) = -2x, \qquad 0 \leqslant x < 1$$
$$f(x) = x - 3, \qquad 1 \leqslant x \leqslant 3$$

Sketch the graph of $y = f(x)$ for $-3 \leqslant x \leqslant 3$.

Answer

The graph of $y = f(x)$ for $0 \leqslant x \leqslant 3$ looks like this:

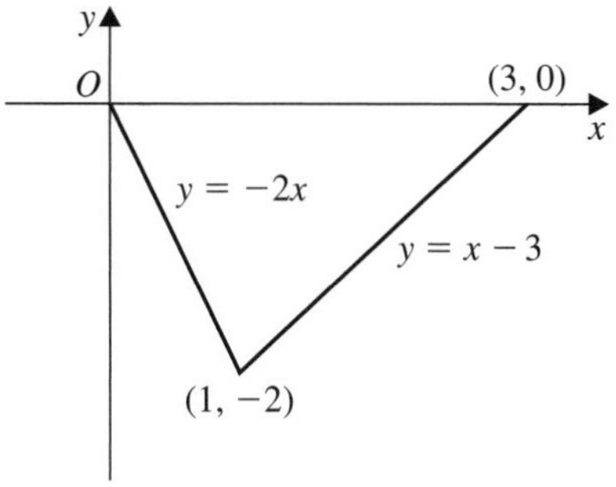

Since f is an odd function, $f(-x) = -f(x)$ so the sketch of $y = f(x)$ for $-3 \leqslant x \leqslant 3$ looks like this:

Using **11**

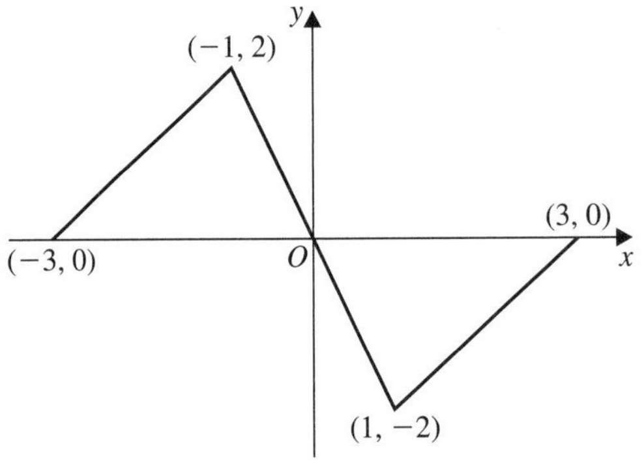

Revision exercise 2

1 For $x \in \mathbb{R}$, the functions f, g and h are given by:

$$f(x) = 2x - 5$$
$$g(x) = \sqrt{(x+3)}, \qquad x > -3$$
$$h(x) = \frac{4}{x+1}, \qquad x \neq -1$$

Find the inverse function in each case.

2 Using the three functions defined in question 1, find the composite functions fg, fh, hg and gf.

3 Find the numbers p and q such that

$$15 + 4x - x^2 \equiv p - (x - q)^2$$

for all real values of x.

State the range of the function f where

$$f: x \mapsto 15 + 4x - x^2, \qquad x \in \mathbb{R}.$$

4 The function f is defined by

$$f: x \mapsto 16 - x^2, \qquad x \in \mathbb{R}$$

(a) State the range of the function f.

(b) Find all the values of x for which

$$ff(x) = 0.$$

5 The diagram shows a sketch of the curve with equation $y = g(x)$ which meets the x-axis at $(\frac{1}{2}, 0)$, $(2, 0)$ and $(5, 0)$.

On separate diagrams, sketch the curve with equation:

(a) $y = |g(x)|$

(b) $y = g(x + 2)$

(c) $y = g(x^2)$

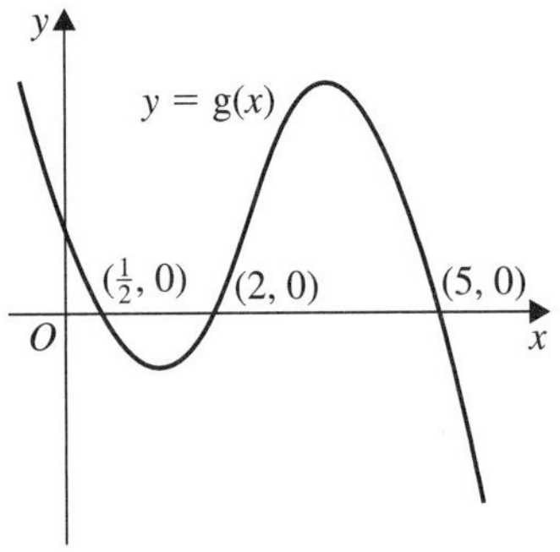

6 On the same axes sketch the graphs of

$$y = -2x \text{ and } y = |3x + 1|.$$

Determine the coordinates of the points of intersection of these graphs.

7 The constants a, b and c are positive. The function f is defined by

$$\mathrm{f}: x \mapsto ax - bx^2, \qquad x \in \mathbb{R},\ x > c.$$

Given that the inverse function f^{-1} exists, find the least possible value of c in terms of a and b.

8 The function f is defined by

$$\mathrm{f}: x \mapsto 1 - \frac{2}{x}, \qquad x \in \mathbb{R},\ x \neq 0,\ x \neq 2.$$

Find in terms of x:

(a) $\mathrm{f}(2x)$

(b) $\mathrm{ff}(x)$

(c) $\mathrm{f}^{-1}(x)$

9 The functions f and g are defined by

$$\mathrm{f}: x \mapsto \tfrac{1}{3}x + 2, \qquad x \in \mathbb{R},$$

$$\mathrm{g}: x \mapsto \frac{1}{1 - x}, \qquad x \in \mathbb{R},\ x \neq 1$$

Find, in similar form:

(a) the composite function gf,

(b) the inverse function f^{-1}, stating its domain.

(c) Sketch the functions f and f^{-1} on the same diagram, together with the line whose equation is $y = x$.

10 The function f is defined by

$$\mathrm{f}: x \mapsto \frac{1}{5x - 2}, \qquad x \in \mathbb{R},\ x \neq \tfrac{2}{5}$$

Find in its simplest form:

(a) $\mathrm{ff}(x)$

(b) $\mathrm{f}^{-1}(x)$

11 Given that $x \in \mathbb{R}$, find three functions f, g and h for which the composite function fgh is such that

$$\mathrm{fgh}: x \mapsto 3x^2 - 12x + 12$$

Find also in terms of x, the composite functions hgf and hfg.

12 The diagram shows a sketch of the curve with equation $y = \mathrm{f}(x)$, where $\mathrm{f}(x) \equiv -(2x - 3)^2$. The curve touches the x-axis at A and meets the y-axis at B.

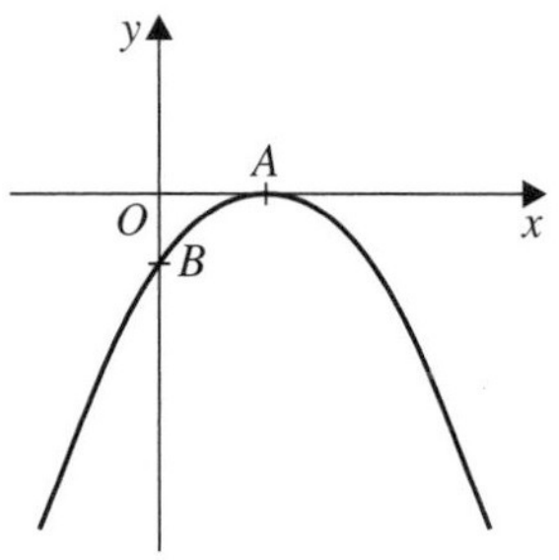

(a) State the coordinates of A and B.

(b) On separate diagrams, draw a sketch of the curves with equations:

(i) $y = \mathrm{f}(x + \frac{3}{2})$

(ii) $y = \mathrm{f}(x - \frac{3}{2})$

(iii) $y = |\mathrm{f}(x)|$

(iv) $y = |\mathrm{f}(x) - 4|$

(v) $y = \mathrm{f}(|x|)$

13 The function f is given by

$$\mathrm{f}: x \mapsto \frac{6}{2x + 1}, \qquad x \in \mathbb{R},\ 1 \leqslant x \leqslant 4$$

(a) Find the range of f.

(b) Sketch the curves with equations $y = \mathrm{f}(x)$ and $y = \mathrm{f}^{-1}(x)$ on the same diagram.

Test yourself

What to review

If your answer is incorrect:

1 Find the inverse of the function f where

$\mathrm{f}: x \mapsto 4 - 3x, \qquad x \in \mathbb{R}$

Review Heinemann Book P2 pages 19–23

---

2 The functions f and g are defined as

$\mathrm{f}: x \mapsto 2x - 3, \qquad x \in \mathbb{R}$

$\mathrm{g}: x \mapsto (3x - 1)^2, \qquad x \in \mathbb{R}$

Find fg and gf.

Review Heinemann Book P2 pages 17–19

3

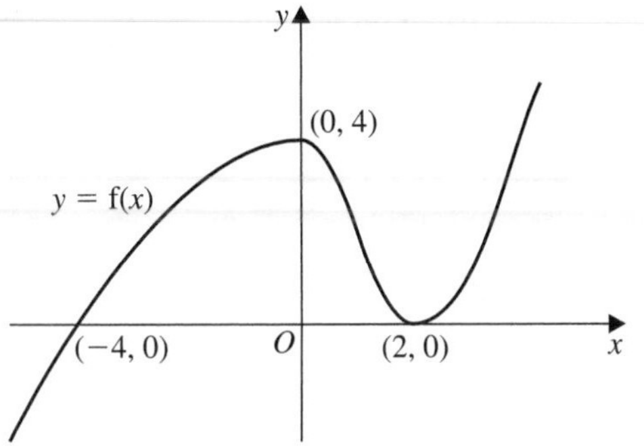

Review Heinemann Book P2 pages 23–27

The diagram shows a sketch of the curve with equation $y = \mathrm{f}(x)$.
The curve has turning points at $(0, 4)$ and $(2, 0)$. It meets the x-axis at $(-4, 0)$.
Sketch the curves with equations:
(a) $y = |\mathrm{f}(x)|$ **(b)** $y = \mathrm{f}(|x|)$

---

4 The functions f and g are defined by

$$\mathrm{f}: x \mapsto 4 - x^2, \quad x \in \mathbb{R}$$
$$\mathrm{g}: x \mapsto \frac{1}{1+x}, \quad x \in \mathbb{R}, x \neq -1$$

Review Heinemann Book P2 pages 17–23

(a) Find $\mathrm{g}^{-1}(x)$.
(b) Solve the equation $\mathrm{ff}(x) = 0$.
(c) Express $\mathrm{fg}(x)$ as a single algebraic fraction.

Test yourself answers

1 $\mathrm{f}^{-1}: x \mapsto \frac{1}{3}(4 - x), x \in \mathbb{R}$ **2** $\mathrm{fg}: x \mapsto 18x^2 - 12x - 1, x \in \mathbb{R}$ $\mathrm{gf}: x \mapsto 36x^2 - 120x + 100, x \in \mathbb{R}$

3 (a)

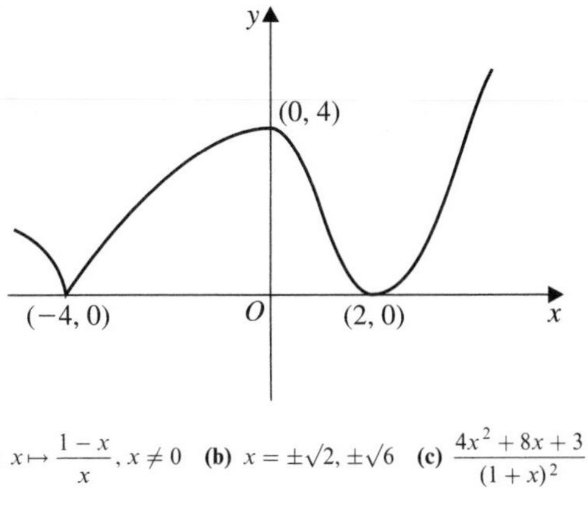

(b)

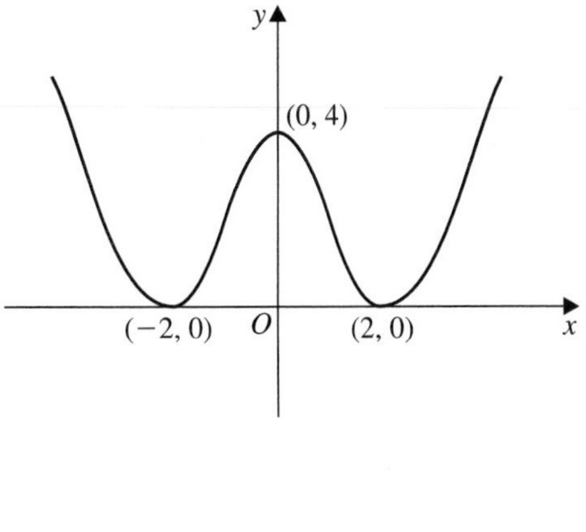

4 (a) $x \mapsto \dfrac{1-x}{x}, x \neq 0$ **(b)** $x = \pm\sqrt{2}, \pm\sqrt{6}$ **(c)** $\dfrac{4x^2 + 8x + 3}{(1+x)^2}$

Sequences and series

3

Key points to remember

1 For the sequence

$u_1, u_2, u_3, \ldots, u_n, \ldots$

a relationship such as $u_n = f(u_{n-1})$ is called a **recurrence relation**.

2 Binomial expressions consist of two terms, e.g. $a + bx$.

3 Pascal's triangular array is:

$$\begin{array}{ccccccccc} & & & & 1 & & & & \\ & & & 1 & & 1 & & & \\ & & 1 & & 2 & & 1 & & \\ & 1 & & 3 & & 3 & & 1 & \\ 1 & & 4 & & 6 & & 4 & & 1 \end{array}$$

. . . . etc . . . .

4 Factorial n, written $n!$, is

$1 \times 2 \times 3 \times \ldots \times (n-1) \times n$.

5 $\binom{n}{r} = {}^nC_r = \dfrac{n!}{r!(n-r)!}$.

6 $(1+x)^n = 1 + \binom{n}{1}x + \binom{n}{2}x^2 + \ldots + \binom{n}{r}x^r + \ldots + x^n$, for $n \in \mathbb{Z}^+$.

7 $(a+b)^n = a^n + \binom{n}{1}a^{n-1}b + \binom{n}{2}a^{n-2}b^2 + \ldots + \binom{n}{r}a^{n-r}b^r + \ldots + b^n$, for $n \in \mathbb{Z}^+$.

Example 1

The terms of a sequence are defined by the recurrence relation

$$u_n = 2(-1)^{n-1}u_{n-1}, \quad u_1 = \tfrac{1}{8}, n \geqslant 1$$

Find u_2, u_3, u_4, u_5.

Answer

$u_1 = \frac{1}{8}$

$u_2 = 2(-1)^1 u_1 = -2u_1 = -2(\frac{1}{8}) = -\frac{1}{4}$ — Using **1**

$u_3 = 2(-1)^2 u_2 = 2u_2 = 2(-\frac{1}{4}) = -\frac{1}{2}$

$u_4 = 2(-1)^3 u_3 = -2u_3 = -2(-\frac{1}{2}) = 1$

$u_5 = 2(-1)^4 u_4 = 2u_4 = 2(1) = 2$

Example 2

A sequence is defined by

$$u_n = \frac{6}{1 + u_{n-1}}, \quad u_1 = 1$$

Determine the values of u_2, u_3 and u_4 and the limiting value of the sequence.

Answer

$$u_2 = \frac{6}{1 + u_1} = \frac{6}{1 + 1} = 3$$

Using **1**

$$u_3 = \frac{6}{1 + u_2} = \frac{6}{1 + 3} = \frac{3}{2}$$

$$u_4 = \frac{6}{1 + u_3} = \frac{6}{1 + \frac{3}{2}} = \frac{6}{\frac{5}{2}} = \frac{12}{5}$$

Let the limiting value be x.
Then, when n is large,

$$u_{n-1} = u_n = x$$

So $x = \dfrac{6}{1 + x}$

That is $x(1 + x) = 6$

$$x^2 + x - 6 = 0$$

$$(x - 2)(x + 3) = 0$$

$$x = 2, -3$$

Reject -3, since clearly all the terms of the sequence are positive.
So the limiting value is 2.

Example 3

Expand $\left(2x - \frac{3}{x^2}\right)^4$ in descending powers of x.

Answer

$(a+b)^4 = a^4 + 4a^3b + 6a^2b^2 + 4ab^3 + b^4$

Using 7 and 3

So $\left(2x - \frac{3}{x^2}\right)^4 = (2x)^4 + 4(2x)^3\left(-\frac{3}{x^2}\right) + 6(2x)^2\left(-\frac{3}{x^2}\right)^2 + 4(2x)\left(-\frac{3}{x^2}\right)^3 + \left(-\frac{3}{x^2}\right)^4$

$$= 16x^4 + 32x^3\left(-\frac{3}{x^2}\right) + 24x^2\left(-\frac{3}{x^2}\right)^2 + 8x\left(-\frac{3}{x^2}\right)^3 + \left(-\frac{3}{x^2}\right)^4$$

$$= 16x^4 - 96x + \frac{216}{x^2} - \frac{216}{x^5} + \frac{81}{x^8}$$

Example 4

In the expansion of $(1-3x)(1+kx)^9$, the coefficient of x^6 is zero.
Find the non-zero value of k.

Answer

$(1-3x)(1+kx)^9$

$$= (1-3x)[1 + 9kx + \ldots + \binom{9}{5}(kx)^5 + \binom{9}{6}(kx)^6 + \ldots + (kx)^9]$$

Using 6

So the term in x^6 is given by

$$\binom{9}{6}(kx)^6 - 3x\binom{9}{5}(kx)^5$$

$$= \frac{9!}{6!\,3!}k^6x^6 - 3x.\ \frac{9!}{5!\,4!}k^5x^5$$

Using 5

$$= \frac{9\times8\times7}{3\times2}k^6x^6 - 3x.\ \frac{9\times8\times7\times6}{4\times3\times2}k^5x^5$$

Using 4

$$= 84k^6x^6 - (3x)126k^5x^5$$

$$= 84k^6x^6 - 378k^5x^6$$

$$= (84k^6 - 378k^5)x^6$$

If the coefficient of x^6 is zero then

$$84k^6 - 378k^5 = 0$$

So $k^5(84k - 378) = 0$

So $k = 0$ or $k = \frac{378}{84} = 4\frac{1}{2}$

As k is non-zero, $k = 4\frac{1}{2}$

Example 5

Given that $A = 1 + 2k$ and $B = 1 - 2k$, prove that

$$A^5 + B^5 = 32 + 10AB(AB - 4)$$

Answer

$$A^5 + B^5 = (1 + 2k)^5 + (1 - 2k)^5$$

$$= [1 + 5(2k) + 10(2k)^2 + 10(2k)^3 + 5(2k)^4 + (2k)^5]$$

Using **6** and **3**

$$+ [1 + 5(-2k) + 10(-2k)^2 + 10(-2k)^3 + 5(-2k)^4 + (-2k)^5]$$

$$= 1 + 10k + 40k^2 + 80k^3 + 80k^4 + 32k^5 + 1 - 10k + 40k^2$$

$$- 80k^3 + 80k^4 - 32k^5$$

$$= 2 + 80k^2 + 160k^4$$

Now $32 + 10AB(AB - 4)$

$$= 32 + 10(1 + 2k)(1 - 2k)[(1 + 2k)(1 - 2k) - 4]$$

$$= 32 + 10(1 - 4k^2)[1 - 4k^2 - 4]$$

Using difference of two squares

$$= 32 + 10(1 - 4k^2)(-3 - 4k^2)$$

$$= 32 + 10(-3 - 4k^2 + 12k^2 + 16k^4)$$

$$= 32 + 10(-3 + 8k^2 + 16k^4)$$

$$= 32 - 30 + 80k^2 + 160k^4$$

$$= 2 + 80k^2 + 160k^4$$

So $A^5 + B^5 = 32 + 10AB(AB - 4)$

Revision exercise 3

1 Investigate the nature of the sequences whose nth term u_n and first term u_1 are:

(a) $u_n = 3u_{n-1} - 2,\ u_1 = 2$

(b) $u_n = (-1)^{n-1}u_{n-1}^2,\ u_1 = 1$

(c) $u_n = (-1)^{n-1}3u_{n-1}^2,\ u_1 = 2$

(d) $u_n = \dfrac{u_{n-1}}{1 + u_{n-1}},\ u_1 = 1$

2 For the sequence $u_1, u_2, u_3, \ldots, u_{n-1}, u_n, \ldots$ the terms are related by

$$u_n = \frac{2}{2 + u_{n-1}}, \quad u_1 = 1$$

(a) Find the exact values of u_2, u_3 and u_4.

(b) Find the limiting value of the sequence.

3 The rth term of a series is u_r.

Given that $u_r = u_{r-1} + 2$ and $u_1 = 3$, find $\sum_{r=1}^{n} u_r$.

4 The rth term of a series is u_r.
Given that $u_r = \frac{1}{2}u_{r-1}$ and $u_1 = 5$, find

(a) $\sum_{r=1}^{n} u_r$

(b) the sum to infinity of the series with first term 5 and rth term u_r.

5 For the sequence $u_1, u_2, u_3, \ldots, u_{n-1}, u_n, \ldots$ the terms are related by

$$2u_n = u_{n-1} + \frac{5}{u_{n-1}}, \quad u_1 = 2$$

Find to 5 decimal places the difference between u_3 and the limiting value of the sequence.

6 For the sequence $u_1, u_2, u_3, \ldots, u_{n-1}, u_n, \ldots$

$$u_n = 5 - \frac{6}{u_{n-1}}, \quad u_1 = 5$$

(a) find u_5 to 4 decimal places,

(b) determine the limiting value of the sequence.

7 Expand $(1 - x)^6$.
Find the value of $(0.999)^6$ using your expansion and giving your answer to 10 significant figures.

8 Expand:

(a) $(2x - 5)^4$ in ascending powers of x,

(b) $(5 - 2x)^5$ in descending powers of x.

9 Obtain, in ascending powers of x as far as the term containing x^3, the expansion of $(2 - 3x)(1 + 2x)^{17}$.

10 The first three terms in the expansion of $(1 + Ax)^n$ in ascending powers of x are 1, $14x$ and $84x^2$.
Find the value of:

(a) n **(b)** A

Hence find the coefficients of the terms in x^3 and x^4 in the expansion.

11 Expand $(1 - x^2)^{15}$ in ascending powers of x up to and including the term in x^6.
Use your expansion with an appropriate value for x to find $(0.9996)^{15}$ giving your final answer to as many decimal places as you can justify, explaining your reasoning.

12 Use the binomial expansion to find the *exact* value of $(0.9)^8$ by expanding $(1 - x)^8$ and choosing an appropriate value for x.
Investigate whether or not your calculator can give the exact value of $(0.9)^8$ directly.

13 The coefficients of x^2 and x^4 are equal when $(1 + x)^n$ is expanded using the binomial series.
Find the value of n.
With this value of n find the coefficients of the terms in x^3 and x^5.

14 The sequence $u_1, u_2, u_3, \ldots, u_{n-1}, u_n, \ldots$ is defined by the recurrence relation

$$u_n = 5u_{n-1} - 48n + 64, \quad u_1 = 16$$

Prove that the formula $u_n = 5^n + 12n - 1$ satisfies the recurrence relation for $n = 2$, 3 and 4.

Test yourself	What to review
	If your answer is incorrect:
1 A sequence of numbers is given by the recurrence relation $u_n = 5u_{n-1} + (u_{n-1})^{-1}$. Given that $u_1 = 1$, find u_2 and u_3 as exact rational numbers.	*Review Heinemann Book P2 pages 37–39*
2 In a sequence of decreasing numbers $u_1, u_2, u_3, \ldots, u_n, \ldots$ $u_n = 1 + \sqrt{(u_{n-1})}, \quad u_1 = 16$ **(a)** Find u_5 to 3 decimal places. **(b)** Prove that the limiting value of the sequence is $a + b\sqrt{5}$ where a and b are rational numbers to be found.	*Review Heinemann Book P2 pages 37–39*
3 Expand $(1 + y)^3$. Hence find the expansion of $(1 + x + 3x^2)^3$ in ascending powers of x.	*Review Heinemann Book P2 pages 39–49*
4 Expand $(1 + 2x)^{17}$ in ascending powers of x as far as the term in x^3.	*Review Heinemann Book P2 pages 39–49*

Test yourself answers

1 $6, 30\frac{1}{6}$ **2 (a)** 2.673 **(b)** $a = \frac{3}{2}, b = \frac{1}{2}$ **3** $1 + 3y + 3y^2 + y^3$; $1 + 3x + 12x^2 + 19x^3 + 36x^4 + 27x^5 + 27x^6$ **4** $1 + 34x + 544x^2 + 5440x^3$

Trigonometry

4

Key points to remember

1 $$\sec x = \frac{1}{\cos x}$$

$$\operatorname{cosec} x = \frac{1}{\sin x}$$

$$\cot x = \frac{1}{\tan x}$$

2 The inverse function of $\sin x$ is $\arcsin x$ which has domain $-1 \leqslant x \leqslant 1$ and range $-\frac{\pi}{2} \leqslant \arcsin x \leqslant \frac{\pi}{2}$.

3 The inverse function of $\cos x$ is $\arccos x$ which has domain $-1 \leqslant x \leqslant 1$ and range $0 \leqslant \arccos x \leqslant \pi$.

4 The inverse function of $\tan x$ is $\arctan x$ which has domain $x \in \mathbb{R}$ and range $-\frac{\pi}{2} < \arctan x < \frac{\pi}{2}$.

5 Pythagoras' theorem can be written

$$\sin^2\theta + \cos^2\theta \equiv 1$$

or $$\sec^2\theta \equiv 1 + \tan^2\theta$$

or $$\operatorname{cosec}^2\theta \equiv 1 + \cot^2\theta$$

6 The compound angle formulae are

$$\sin(A+B) \equiv \sin A\cos B + \cos A\sin B$$
$$\sin(A-B) \equiv \sin A\cos B - \cos A\sin B$$
$$\cos(A+B) \equiv \cos A\cos B - \sin A\sin B$$
$$\cos(A-B) \equiv \cos A\cos B + \sin A\sin B$$
$$\tan(A+B) \equiv \frac{\tan A + \tan B}{1 - \tan A\tan B}$$
$$\tan(A-B) \equiv \frac{\tan A - \tan B}{1 + \tan A\tan B}$$

7 The double angle formulae are

$$\sin 2A \equiv 2\sin A\cos A$$
$$\cos 2A \equiv \cos^2 A - \sin^2 A$$
$$\equiv 2\cos^2 A - 1$$
$$\equiv 1 - 2\sin^2 A$$
$$\tan 2A \equiv \frac{2\tan A}{1-\tan^2 A}$$

8 The half angle formulae are

$$\sin^2 \tfrac{1}{2}\theta \equiv \tfrac{1}{2}(1-\cos\theta)$$
$$\cos^2 \tfrac{1}{2}\theta \equiv \tfrac{1}{2}(1+\cos\theta)$$

9 The sum $\rightarrow$ product formulae are

$$\sin P + \sin Q \equiv 2\sin\frac{P+Q}{2}\cos\frac{P-Q}{2}$$

$$\sin P - \sin Q \equiv 2\cos\frac{P+Q}{2}\sin\frac{P-Q}{2}$$

$$\cos P + \cos Q \equiv 2\cos\frac{P+Q}{2}\cos\frac{P-Q}{2}$$

$$\cos Q - \cos P \equiv 2\sin\frac{P+Q}{2}\sin\frac{P-Q}{2}$$

10 The product $\rightarrow$ sum formulae are

$$2\sin A\cos B \equiv \sin(A+B) + \sin(A-B)$$
$$2\cos A\sin B \equiv \sin(A+B) - \sin(A-B)$$
$$2\cos A\cos B \equiv \cos(A+B) + \cos(A-B)$$
$$2\sin A\sin B \equiv \cos(A-B) - \cos(A+B)$$

11 If $a\cos\theta + b\sin\theta \equiv R\cos(\theta+\alpha)$ where $a = R\cos\alpha$ and $b = -R\sin\alpha$

then $R = \sqrt{(a^2+b^2)}$ and $\tan\alpha = -\dfrac{b}{a}$.

12 If $a\cos\theta + b\sin\theta \equiv R\sin(\theta+\beta)$ where $a = R\sin\beta$ and $b = R\cos\beta$

then $R = \sqrt{(a^2+b^2)}$ and $\tan\beta = \dfrac{a}{b}$.

Example 1

Solve, for $0 \leqslant x \leqslant 540°$, $\sin \frac{3}{2}x = \sin x$

Answer

$$\sin \tfrac{3}{2}x = \sin x$$

$$\Rightarrow \quad \sin \tfrac{3}{2}x - \sin x = 0$$

So $$2\cos \frac{\frac{3}{2}x + x}{2} \sin \frac{\frac{3}{2}x - x}{2} = 0$$

Using **9**

$$\Rightarrow \quad 2\cos \frac{5x}{4} \sin \frac{x}{4} = 0$$

$$\Rightarrow \quad \cos \frac{5x}{4} = 0 \text{ or } \sin \frac{x}{4} = 0$$

$$\cos \frac{5x}{4} = 0 \Rightarrow \frac{5x}{4} = 90°, 270°, 450°, 630°, \ldots$$

From the graph of $\cos x$

$$\Rightarrow x = 72°, 216°, 360°, 504°$$

$$\sin \frac{x}{4} = 0 \Rightarrow \frac{x}{4} = 0, 180°, 360°, 540°, \ldots$$

From the graph of $\sin x$

$$\Rightarrow x = 0 \text{ only in the given range}$$

So the solutions are

$$x = 0, 72°, 216°, 360°, 504°$$

Example 2

Solve, for $0 \leqslant y \leqslant 540°$, $3\sin y = 2\cos(60° - y)$.

Answer

$$\cos(60° - y) = \cos 60° \cos y + \sin 60° \sin y$$

Using **6**

$$= \tfrac{1}{2}\cos y + \frac{\sqrt{3}}{2}\sin y$$

Using the 1, 2, $\sqrt{3}$ triangle

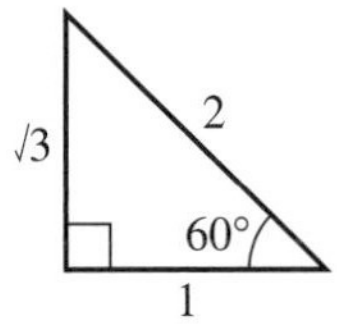

So $3\sin y = 2\cos(60° - y)$

$$\Rightarrow \quad 3\sin y = 2\left(\tfrac{1}{2}\cos y + \frac{\sqrt{3}}{2}\sin y\right)$$

$$3\sin y = \cos y + \sqrt{3}\sin y$$

$$(3 - \sqrt{3})\sin y = \cos y$$

$$\tan y = \frac{1}{3 - \sqrt{3}}$$

Using $\dfrac{\sin x}{\cos x} = \tan x$

$$\Rightarrow \quad y = 38.3°, 218.3°, 398.3°$$

Example 3

Prove that $\arcsin \dfrac{1}{\sqrt{5}} + \operatorname{arccot} 3 = \arctan 1$, where all three angles are acute.

Answer

Let $\alpha = \arcsin \dfrac{1}{\sqrt{5}}$ and $\beta = \operatorname{arccot} 3$

Then $\sin \alpha = \dfrac{1}{\sqrt{5}}$ and $\cot \beta = 3$

Using the definitions of $\arcsin x$ and $\operatorname{arccot} x$

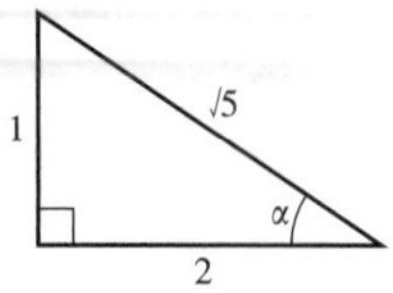

Since α is acute it can lie in a right angled triangle with opposite side 1 and hypotenuse $\sqrt{5}$.

The length of the third side is

$$\sqrt{(5-1)} = \sqrt{4} = 2$$

Using Pythagoras

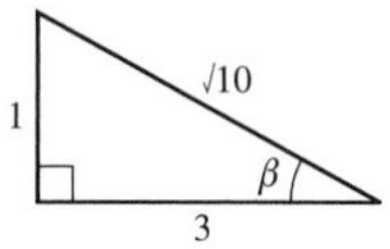

Since β is acute it can lie in a right angled triangle with adjacent side 3 and opposite side 1.

The length of the third side is

$$\sqrt{(9+1)} = \sqrt{10}$$

Using Pythagoras

Now
$$\tan(\alpha+\beta) = \frac{\tan\alpha + \tan\beta}{1 - \tan\alpha\tan\beta}$$

Using **6**

$$= \frac{\frac{1}{2}+\frac{1}{3}}{1-\frac{1}{2}\times\frac{1}{3}}$$

$$= \frac{\frac{5}{6}}{\frac{5}{6}} = 1$$

So $\tan(\alpha+\beta) = 1$
Hence $\alpha + \beta = \arctan 1$
That is

$$\arcsin \frac{1}{\sqrt{5}} + \operatorname{arccot} 3 = \arctan 1$$

as required.

Example 4

Prove that $8\cos^4\theta \equiv \cos 4\theta + 4\cos 2\theta + 3$

Answer

$\cos 4\theta = 2\cos^2 2\theta - 1$

Using **7**

$$= 2(2\cos^2\theta - 1)^2 - 1$$

Using **7** again

$$= 2(4\cos^4\theta - 4\cos^2\theta + 1) - 1$$
$$= 8\cos^4\theta - 8\cos^2\theta + 2 - 1$$
$$= 8\cos^4\theta - 8\cos^2\theta + 1$$

So $\cos 4\theta + 4\cos 2\theta + 3$

$$= (8\cos^4\theta - 8\cos^2\theta + 1) + 4(2\cos^2\theta - 1) + 3$$

Using **7** again

$$= 8\cos^4\theta - 8\cos^2\theta + 1 + 8\cos^2\theta - 4 + 3$$
$$= 8\cos^4\theta, \text{ as required.}$$

Example 5

(a) Express $399\cos x + 40\sin x$ in the form $R\cos(x - \alpha)$ where $R > 0$ and $0 < \alpha < \frac{\pi}{2}$.

(b) Solve the equation

$$399\cos x + 40\sin x = 100$$

for $0 < x < 2\pi$.

Answer

(a) Let $399\cos x + 40\sin x \equiv R\cos(x - \alpha)$

Then $399\cos x + 40\sin x \equiv R\cos x\cos\alpha + R\sin x\sin\alpha$ — Using **6**

So comparing coefficients

$$R\cos\alpha = 399 \text{ and } R\sin\alpha = 40$$

So $R^2\cos^2\alpha + R^2\sin^2\alpha = 399^2 + 40^2$

$$R^2(\cos^2\alpha + \sin^2\alpha) = 159\,201 + 1600$$

$$R^2 = 160\,801$$ — Using **5**

$$R = 401$$

$$\frac{R\sin\alpha}{R\cos\alpha} = \frac{40}{399}$$

$$\tan\alpha = \frac{40}{399}$$ — Using $\frac{\sin\alpha}{\cos\alpha} = \tan\alpha$

$$\alpha = 0.0999 \text{ radians}$$

So: $399\cos x + 40\sin x = 401\cos(x - 0.0999)$

(b) $399\cos x + 40\sin x = 100$

So $401\cos(x - 0.0999) = 100$ — Using **(a)**

$$\cos(x - 0.0999) = \tfrac{100}{401}$$

$$x - 0.0999 = 1.3188 \text{ or } 4.9644$$

$$x = 1.42 \text{ or } 5.06 \text{ (2 d.p.)}$$

Revision exercise 4

1 Find the values of x for which

$$\cos 3x + \cos x = \sin 2x, \qquad 0 < x < 360°$$

2 Starting with $\sin(A - B) \equiv \sin A\cos B - \cos A\sin B$,

and $\cos(A - B) \equiv \cos A\cos B + \sin A\sin B$,

prove that

$$\tan(A - B) \equiv \frac{\tan A - \tan B}{1 + \tan A\tan B}.$$

Hence, or otherwise, find the two values of x in the interval $0 < x < 180°$ for which

$$\tan x - \tan(x - 30°) = 2\tan 30°.$$

3 Find the range of the function f, where

$$f(x) = 8\cos x + 15\sin x, \qquad x \in \mathbb{R}.$$

4 Solve the equation

$$\cos x - \sqrt{3}\sin x = \sqrt{2} \qquad \text{for } -180^\circ \leqslant x \leqslant 180^\circ.$$

5 Find in radians for $0 \leqslant x \leqslant 2\pi$ the values of x for which:

(a) $\cos x = \sin 3x$

(b) $\cos x + \cos 7x = \cos 4x$

(c) $\sin x - \cos x = 1$

6 Given that $\cos\theta = \frac{24}{25}$, find the possible values of:

(a) $\sin\dfrac{\theta}{2}$ **(b)** $\cos\dfrac{\theta}{2}$

7 Prove that:

(a) $\operatorname{cosec}\theta + \cot\theta \equiv \cot\dfrac{\theta}{2}$

(b) $\sin\dfrac{3x}{2} \equiv \sin\dfrac{x}{2}(1 + 2\cos x)$

(c) $(\sin A + \cos A)(\cos B - \sin B) \equiv \sin(A - B) + \cos(A + B)$

8 Without tables or a calculator prove that:

(a) $\sin 10^\circ + \sin 50^\circ = \sin 70^\circ$

(b) $\tan 75^\circ - \tan 45^\circ = \tan 60^\circ + \tan 45^\circ$

For questions 9–16, solve the equations giving all values in the interval $0 \leqslant x \leqslant 360^\circ$.

9 $\tan x = 2\sin x$

10 $\cot x = 2\sin x$

11 $\sin x\cos(60^\circ - x) = 0.4$

12 $\sin(2x + 30^\circ) = \cos(2x - 30^\circ)$

13 $4\sin 2x = 5\sin x$

14 $\sin 2x\cos x + \cos 2x\sin x = \sin(x + 20^\circ)$

15 $6\cos x - 8\sin x = 5$

16 $2\sin x + 3\cos x = 3$

For questions 17–23 find the values of x in radians, for $0 \leqslant x \leqslant 2\pi$, that satisfy the equation.

17 $\cos^2 x - 3\sin x = 2$

18 $3\sin 2x = 2\tan x$

19 $\cos x\cot x = 1 - \sin x$

20 $\sin x + \cos x = 0.5$

21 $5\sin x - 12\cos x = 7$

22 $4\sin 2x + \sin 3x = 0$

23 $\tan x + 3\cot x = 5\sec x$

24 The acute angles A and B are such that $\tan A = \frac{4}{3}$ and $\tan B = 7$.

Prove that $A + B = \dfrac{3\pi}{4}$.

25 Given that the angles are acute, prove that

$$\arctan \tfrac{1}{3} + \arctan \tfrac{1}{7} = \arctan \tfrac{1}{2}.$$

26 Prove that

$$2\sin^2 P \sin^2 Q + 2\cos^2 P \cos^2 Q \equiv 1 + \cos 2P \cos 2Q.$$

Test yourself

Test yourself	What to review
	If your answer is incorrect:
1 Find, in terms of π, the values of x for which $\cos\left(3x - \dfrac{\pi}{3}\right) = \cos\left(x + \dfrac{\pi}{6}\right)$ and $0 \leqslant x \leqslant 2\pi$.	*Review Heinemann Book P2 pages 61–67*
2 Find, in radians in terms of π, the values of x, $-2\pi \leqslant x \leqslant 2\pi$, for which $\sin 5x + \sin 3x = 0$.	*Review Heinemann Book P2 pages 71–73*
3 Given that $\sin\theta = -\frac{4}{5}$, find the possible values of **(a)** $\cos 2\theta$ **(b)** $\tan 2\theta$.	*Review Heinemann Book P2 pages 67–68*
4 Without tables or a calculator, prove that $\cos 80° + \cos 40° = \sin 70°$.	*Review Heinemann Book P2 pages 61–73*
5 Solve for x, $0 \leqslant x \leqslant 360°$, the equation $3\sec^2 x - 5\tan x - 5 = 0$	*Review Heinemann Book P2 pages 57–61*
6 Find the values of x, for $0 \leqslant x \leqslant 2\pi$, that satisfy the equation $\tan 2x = \tan x$	*Review Heinemann Book P2 pages 67–71*

Test yourself answers

1 $\dfrac{\pi}{24}, \dfrac{\pi}{4}, \dfrac{13\pi}{24}, \dfrac{25\pi}{24}, \dfrac{5\pi}{4}, \dfrac{37\pi}{24}$ **2** $\pm 2\pi, \pm\dfrac{7\pi}{4}, \pm\dfrac{3\pi}{2}, \pm\dfrac{5\pi}{4}, \pm\pi, \pm\dfrac{3\pi}{4}, \pm\dfrac{\pi}{2}, \pm\dfrac{\pi}{4}, 0$ **3 (a)** $-\frac{7}{25}$ **(b)** $\pm\frac{24}{7}$

5 63.4°, 243.4°, 161.6°, 341.6° **6** 0, 3.14, 6.28

Exponentials and logarithms

5

Key points to remember

1 A function $f: x \mapsto a^x$, where a is a constant is called an exponential function.

2 The function $f: x \mapsto e^x$, $x \in \mathbb{R}$, is called *the* exponential function.

3 The graph of $y = e^x$, $x \in \mathbb{R}$, looks like this:

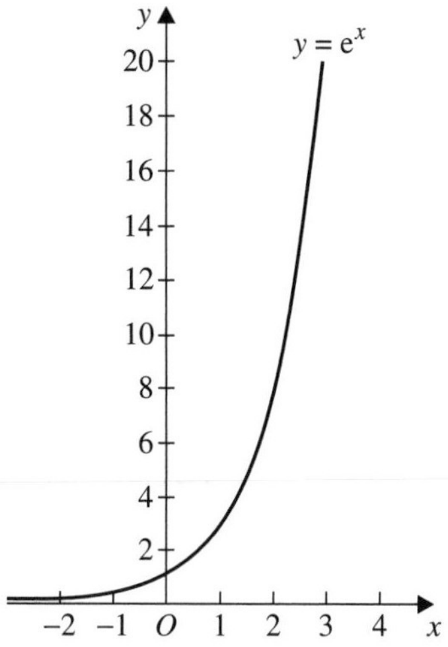

4 A logarithm is another name for a power or index or exponent.

5 Logarithms in base e are called natural logarithms.

6 $\log_e x$ is usually written as $\ln x$.

7 If $f: x \mapsto e^x$, $x \in \mathbb{R}$, then $f^{-1}: x \mapsto \ln x$, $x > 0$.

8 The graph of $y = \ln x$, $x > 0$, looks like this:

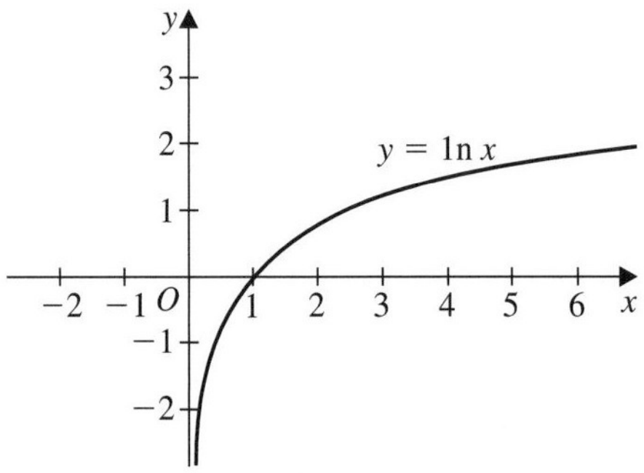

9 The laws of logarithms are:

(i) $\log_a xy = \log_a x + \log_a y$

(ii) $\log_a \frac{x}{y} = \log_a x - \log_a y$

(iii) $\log_a x^n = n \log_a x$

(iv) $\log_a a = 1$

(v) $\log_a 1 = 0$

10 $\log_{10} x$ is usually written $\lg x$

11 $\log_a b = \frac{\log_c b}{\log_c a}$

12 An equation of the form $a^x = b$ is solved by taking logarithms of both sides.

Example 1

Find the value of x for which

$$4^{2x+3} = 11^{x+2}$$

Answer

$$\lg(4^{2x+3}) = \lg(11^{x+2})$$ Using **12**

$$(2x+3)\lg 4 = (x+2)\lg 11$$ Using **9** (iii)

$$2x\lg 4 + 3\lg 4 = x\lg 11 + 2\lg 11$$

$$2x\lg 4 - x\lg 11 = 2\lg 11 - 3\lg 4$$

$$x(2\lg 4 - \lg 11) = 2\lg 11 - 3\lg 4$$

$$x = \frac{2\lg 11 - 3\lg 4}{2\lg 4 - \lg 11}$$

$$= 1.70 \text{ (3 s.f.)}$$

Example 2

The function f is defined by

$$f: x \mapsto e^{\sin x}, \qquad x \in \mathbb{R}, 0 \leqslant x \leqslant \frac{\pi}{2}$$

(a) Sketch the curve with equation $y = f(x)$.
(b) Define the inverse function f^{-1}.
(c) Explain why the function g defined by

$$g: x \mapsto e^{\sin x}, \qquad x \in \mathbb{R}, 0 \leqslant x \leqslant \pi$$

has no inverse function.

Answer

(a) When $x = 0$, $y = 1$

When $x = \frac{\pi}{2}$, $y = e^{\sin\frac{\pi}{2}} = e^1 = e$

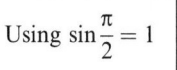

Using $\sin\frac{\pi}{2} = 1$

The curve looks like this:

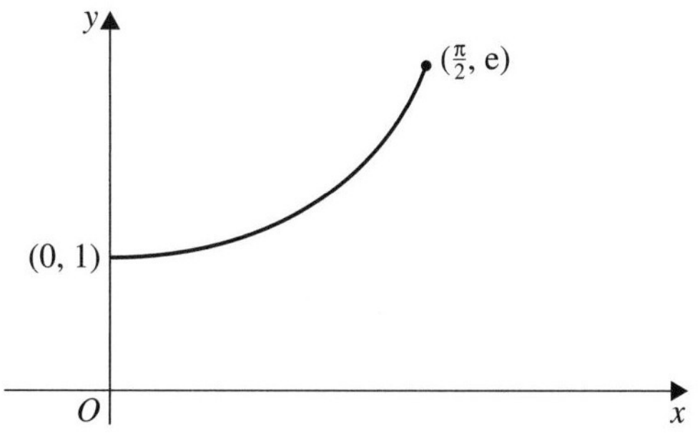

(b) Let $y = e^{\sin x}$
Then $\ln y = \ln e^{\sin x}$
$\Rightarrow \quad \ln y = \sin x$
So $\quad x = \arcsin(\ln y)$

Using 9 (iii) and (iv)

Thus $g^{-1}: x \mapsto \arcsin(\ln x), \qquad x \in \mathbb{R}, 1 \leqslant x \leqslant e$

(c) $g(\pi) = e^{\sin \pi} = e^0 = 1$
The graph of g looks like this:

Using $\sin \pi = 0$

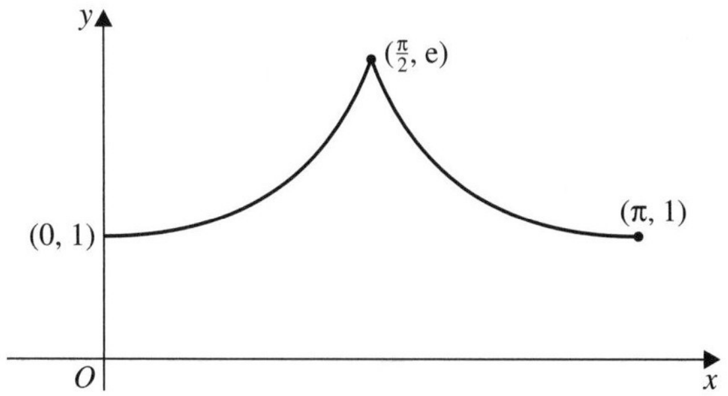

g is **not** one–one and so has no inverse function.

Example 3

Given that $\ln 2 = p$ and $\ln 3 = q$, express in terms of p and q:

(a) $\ln 6$ **(b)** $\ln \frac{243}{32}$

(c) $\ln 432$ **(d)** $\ln 24\text{e}$

(e) $\ln 54\text{e}^{-\frac{1}{2}}$ **(f)** $\ln \frac{9}{16} - \ln \frac{16}{9}$

Answer

(a) $\ln 6 = \ln(2 \times 3) = \ln 2 + \ln 3$ — Using **9** (i)

$= p + q$

(b) $\ln \frac{243}{32} = \ln 243 - \ln 32$ — Using **9** (ii)

$= \ln 3^5 - \ln 2^5 = 5\ln 3 - 5\ln 2$ — Using **9** (iii)

$= 5(\ln 3 - \ln 2)$

$= 5(q - p)$

(c) $\ln 432 = \ln(16 \times 27) = \ln 16 + \ln 27$ — Using **9** (i)

$= \ln 2^4 + \ln 3^3 = 4\ln 2 + 3\ln 3$ — Using **9** (iii)

$= 4p + 3q$

(d) $\ln 24\text{e} = \ln 24 + \ln \text{e}$ — Using **9** (i)

$= \ln 24 + 1$ — Using **9** (iv)

$= \ln(3 \times 8) + 1 = \ln 3 + \ln 8 + 1$ — Using **9** (i)

$= \ln 3 + \ln 2^3 + 1 = \ln 3 + 3\ln 2 + 1$ — Using **9** (iii)

$= q + 3p + 1$

(e) $\ln 54\text{e}^{-\frac{1}{2}} = \ln 54 + \ln \text{e}^{-\frac{1}{2}}$ — Using **9** (i)

$= \ln(2 \times 27) - \frac{1}{2}\ln \text{e}$ — Using **9** (iii)

$= \ln 2 + \ln 27 - \frac{1}{2}\ln \text{e}$ — Using **9** (i)

$= \ln 2 + \ln 3^3 - \frac{1}{2}$ — Using **9** (iv)

$= \ln 2 + 3\ln 3 - \frac{1}{2}$ — Using **9** (iii)

$= p + 3q - \frac{1}{2}$

(f) $\ln \frac{9}{16} - \ln \frac{16}{9}$

$= \ln\left(\frac{9}{16} \div \frac{16}{9}\right)$ — Using **9** (ii)

$= \ln\left(\frac{9}{16} \times \frac{9}{16}\right) = \ln\left(\frac{9}{16}\right)^2$

$= 2\ln \frac{9}{16} = 2[\ln 9 - \ln 16]$ — Using **9** (iii) and (ii)

$= 2[\ln 3^2 - \ln 2^4] = 2[2\ln 3 - 4\ln 2]$ — Using **9** (iii)

$= 4\ln 3 - 8\ln 2$

$= 4q - 8p$

Example 4

The variables x and y are related by the equation

$$y = ax^n$$

where a and n are constants. Given that $y = 650$ when $x = 4$ and that $y = 6360$ when $x = 10$, find the values of a and n.

Answer

$$y = ax^n$$

So $\ln y = \ln(ax^n)$

$\Rightarrow \ln y = \ln a + \ln x^n$ — Using 9 (i)

$\Rightarrow \ln y = \ln a + n\ln x$ — Using 9 (iii)

$x = 4,\ y = 650 \Rightarrow \ln 650 = \ln a + n\ln 4$ ①

$x = 10,\ y = 6360 \Rightarrow \ln 6360 = \ln a + n\ln 10$ ②

② − ① $\ln 6360 - \ln 650 = n\ln 10 - n\ln 4$

$\Rightarrow \ln\frac{6360}{650} = n\ln\frac{10}{4}$ — Using 9 (ii)

$\Rightarrow n = \dfrac{\ln\frac{6360}{650}}{\ln\frac{10}{4}} = 2.49 \text{ (3 s.f.)}$

From ① $\ln a = \ln 650 - n\ln 4$

$= \ln 650 - 2.489\ln 4$

$= 3.026\ldots$

$a = e^{3.026\ldots}$ — Using 7

$a = 20.6 \text{ (3 s.f.)}$

Revision exercise 5

1 Given that $\ln 4 = p$ and $\ln 5 = q$, express in terms of either p or q or both p and q:

(a) $\ln\frac{1}{125}$ **(b)** $\ln 1.25$ **(c)** $\ln 2.56$ **(d)** $\ln 10$

2 Given that $2^m \times 7^n = 8\,605\,184$, where m and n are integers, find the values of m and n.

3 Solve the equations giving answers to 3 significant figures:

(a) $2^x = \frac{1}{10}$ **(b)** $5^x + 5^{-x} = 6$

4 Given that $pq^2 = e$, prove that the sum of the first 5 terms of the arithmetic series with first term $\ln p^2$ and common difference $2\ln q$ is 10.

5 The function f is defined by

$$f : x \mapsto 3^x, \quad x \in \mathbb{R}$$

(a) Write down the values of f(0) and f(−2).

(b) Given that $f(k) = 5$, find k to 3 significant figures.

(c) Define the inverse function f^{-1} and state its domain.

6 Express $\log_8 x$ in terms of logarithms to the base 2.
Hence, or otherwise, solve the equation

$$\log_8 x + \log_2 x = 3$$

7 Solve for p and q the simultaneous equations

$$\log_q p = 2$$
$$5q = p + 12 \log_p q$$

8 The function g is given by

$$g(x) = e^{-4x}, \qquad x \in \mathbb{R}$$

(a) State the range of g.

(b) Find $g^{-1}(x)$ in terms of x and state the domain of g^{-1}.

(c) Evaluate $gg(1)$, giving your answer to 3 decimal places.

9 Find as natural logarithms the roots of the equation
$2e^x + 4e^{-x} = 9$.

10 The variables x and y are related by the equation $y = kx^c$, where k and c are constants.
Given that $y = 1000$ when $x = 3$ and $y = 61\,200$ when $x = 8$, find the values of k and c.

11 Solve the equations:

(a) $13^{x+1} = 5^{2x-1}$ **(b)** $\lg(3x + 2) = 2.3$

12 Find the non-zero values of x and y for which $x^y = y^{3x}$ and $y^3 = x^2$.

13 Find the exact values of:

(a) $\log_{625} 25$ **(b)** $\log_2 4 - \log_4 2$.

14 Solve the equation

$$3^y - 3^{-y} = 3$$

15 **(a)** Simplify $\ln\left(\dfrac{a-b}{a+b}\right)^2 \div \ln\left(\dfrac{a-b}{a+b}\right)$

(b) Given that $p^2 + q^2 = 14pq$
prove that $\lg(p + q) - \lg 4 = \frac{1}{2}(\lg p + \lg q)$

16 On separate diagrams sketch the curve with equation

$$\ln y = kx$$

(a) when $k = 2$ **(b)** when $k = -2$.

17 On separate diagrams sketch the curve with equation

$y = \ln(kx)$

(a) when $k = 2$ and $x > 0$

(b) when $k = -2$ and $x < 0$

18 Given that $A^2 + B^2 = 6AB$, prove that

$2\ln(A + B) - \ln A = \ln(8B)$

Test yourself

What to review

If your answer is incorrect:

1 Given that $\ln 4 = p$ and $\ln 5 = q$, express in terms of p or q or both p and q:

(a) $\ln 32$

(b) $\ln 100$

Review Heinemann Book P2 pages 106–110

---

2 Solve, giving your answer to 3 significant figures, the equation

$3^x = 14$

Review Heinemann Book P2 pages 110–113

---

3 Solve the equation

$10^{x-2} = 2^{x+2}$

giving your answer to 3 significant figures.

Review Heinemann Book P2 pages 110–113

---

4 The function f is defined by

$\mathrm{f}: x \mapsto 1 + \ln(3x + 4), \quad x \in \mathbb{R}, x > -\frac{4}{3}$

(a) Find the range of f.

(b) Find f^{-1} and state its domain.

Review Heinemann Book P2 pages 103–106

---

5 Find the exact value of

$\log_9 243$

Review Heinemann Book P2 pages 108–109

---

6 Solve the equation

$2^{2x} + 2^x - 12 = 0$

Review Heinemann Book P2 pages 110–113

Test yourself answers

1 (a) $\frac{5}{2}p$ **(b)** $p + 2q$ **2** 2.40 **3** 3.72 **4 (a)** $\mathbb{R}$ **(b)** $\mathrm{f}^{-1}: x \mapsto \frac{e^{x-1} - 4}{3}, \quad x \in \mathbb{R}$ **5** $2\frac{1}{2}$ **6** 1.58 (2 d.p.)

Differentiation 6

Key points to remember

1 $\dfrac{d(e^x)}{dx} = e^x$

2 $\dfrac{d(ke^x)}{dx} = ke^x$, where k is a constant.

3 $\dfrac{d(\ln x)}{dx} = \dfrac{1}{x}$

4 $\dfrac{d(\ln kx)}{dx} = \dfrac{1}{x}$, where k is a constant.

5 $\dfrac{d(\log_a x)}{dx} = \dfrac{1}{x \ln a}$

6 The tangent to the curve with equation $y = f(x)$ at the point (a, b) has equation

$$y - b = f'(a)(x - a)$$

7 The normal to the curve with equation $y = f(x)$ at the point (a, b) has equation

$$y - b = \frac{-1}{f'(a)}(x - a)$$

Example 1

Differentiate $\frac{1}{7}e^x$ with respect to x.

Answer

Let $y = \frac{1}{7}e^x$

$$\frac{dy}{dx} = \frac{1}{7}\frac{d(e^x)}{dx}$$

Using **1**

$$= \frac{1}{7}e^x$$

Example 2

Differentiate $\ln 5x^2$ with respect to x.

Answer

Let $y = \ln 5x^2$

$= \ln 5 + \ln x^2$ — Using $\ln(ab) = \ln a + \ln b$

$y = \ln 5 + 2\ln x$ — Using $\ln a^b = b\ln a$

So $\dfrac{dy}{dx} = 0 + 2 \times \dfrac{1}{x} = \dfrac{2}{x}$ — Using **3**

Example 3

Differentiate $\ln\left(\dfrac{e^x}{2x^4}\right)$ with respect to x.

Answer

Let $y = \ln\left(\dfrac{e^x}{2x^4}\right)$

$= \ln e^x - \ln 2x^4$ — Using $\ln\dfrac{a}{b} = \ln a - \ln b$

$= \ln e^x - (\ln 2 + \ln x^4)$ — Using $\ln ab = \ln a + \ln b$

$= \ln e^x - \ln 2 - \ln x^4$

$y = x\ln e - \ln 2 - 4\ln x$ — Using $\ln a^b = b\ln a$

So $\dfrac{dy}{dx} = \ln e - 0 - 4 \times \dfrac{1}{x}$ — Using **3**

$= 1 - \dfrac{4}{x}$ — Using $\ln e = 1$

Example 4

Given that $y = Ae^x + Bx$, prove that

$$(x-1)\frac{d^2y}{dx^2} - x\frac{dy}{dx} + y = 0$$

Answer

$y = Ae^x + Bx$

So $\dfrac{dy}{dx} = Ae^x + B$ — Using **2**

and $\dfrac{d^2y}{dx^2} = Ae^x$ — Using **2**

Now $(x-1)\dfrac{d^2y}{dx^2} - x\dfrac{dy}{dx} + y$

$= (x-1)Ae^x - x(Ae^x + B) + (Ae^x + Bx)$

$= Axe^x - Ae^x - Axe^x - Bx + Ae^x + Bx = 0$, as required.

Example 5

The curve with equation $y = \ln x + 3$ meets the x-axis at the point A.
The point B lies on the curve and has x-coordinate 1.
The tangent to the curve at A and the normal to the curve at B meet at the point C.
Find the coordinates of C.

Answer

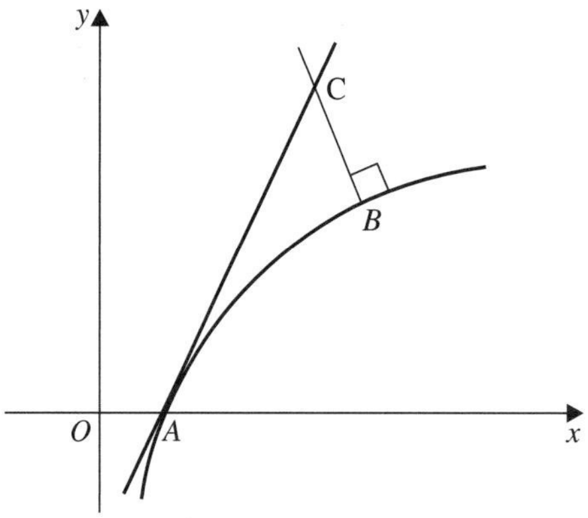

The x-coordinate of A is given by

$$0 = \ln x + 3$$
$$\Rightarrow \quad \ln x = -3$$
$$\Rightarrow \quad x = e^{-3}$$

Using $\ln x$ is the inverse of e^x

So A is the point $(e^{-3}, 0)$.

The y-coordinate of B is given by
$$y = \ln 1 + 3 = 0 + 3$$
So B is the point (1, 3).

$$y = \ln x + 3$$

So $\quad \dfrac{dy}{dx} = \dfrac{1}{x} + 0 = \dfrac{1}{x}$

Using **3**

At A, $\dfrac{dy}{dx} = \dfrac{1}{e^{-3}} = e^3$

So the equation of the tangent at A is

$$y - 0 = e^3(x - e^{-3})$$

Using **6**

i.e. $\quad y = e^3x - 1 \qquad (1)$

At B, $\dfrac{dy}{dx} = \dfrac{1}{1} = 1$

So the equation of the normal at B is

$$y - 3 = -1(x - 1)$$

Using **7**

$$y - 3 = -x + 1$$
$$y = 4 - x \qquad (2)$$

① cuts ② where

$$e^3x - 1 = 4 - x$$
$$x(e^3 + 1) = 5$$
$$x = \frac{5}{e^3 + 1}$$

Substitute in ②:

$$y = 4 - \frac{5}{e^3 + 1}$$
$$= \frac{4e^3 + 4 - 5}{e^3 + 1} = \frac{4e^3 - 1}{e^3 + 1}$$

So C is the point $\left(\frac{5}{e^3 + 1}, \frac{4e^3 - 1}{e^3 + 1}\right)$

Example 6

The curve C has equation

$$y = 2x^2 - \ln x, \qquad x > 0$$

Find the coordinates of the turning point on C and establish whether it is a maximum or a minimum.

Answer

$$y = 2x^2 - \ln x$$
$$\Rightarrow \quad \frac{dy}{dx} = 4x - \frac{1}{x}$$

Using **3**

Turning points occur where $\frac{dy}{dx} = 0$

i.e. where $4x - \frac{1}{x} = 0$

$$\Rightarrow \quad 4x^2 - 1 = 0$$
$$\Rightarrow \quad x^2 = \tfrac{1}{4}$$
$$x = \pm\tfrac{1}{2}$$

Since $x > 0$, reject $x = -\frac{1}{2}$

So at $x = \frac{1}{2}$, $y = \frac{1}{2} - \ln\frac{1}{2} = \frac{1}{2} + \ln 2$

Using $\ln\frac{a}{b} = \ln a - \ln b$

$$\frac{dy}{dx} = 4x - \frac{1}{x} = 4x - x^{-1}$$
$$\frac{d^2y}{dx^2} = 4 + x^{-2} = 4 + \frac{1}{x^2}$$

At $x = \frac{1}{2}$, $\frac{d^2y}{dx^2} = 4 + \frac{1}{\frac{1}{4}} = 4 + 4 = 8 > 0$

Since $\frac{d^2y}{dx^2} > 0$, the point is a minimum.

The turning point has coordinates $(\frac{1}{2}, \frac{1}{2} + \ln 2)$ and is a minimum.

Revision exercise 6

In questions 1–8 find $\frac{\mathrm{d}y}{\mathrm{d}x}$.

1 $y = 4\mathrm{e}^x$ **2** $y = -\frac{1}{3}\mathrm{e}^x$ **3** $y = 3x^2 - 7\mathrm{e}^x$

4 $y = \frac{1}{2}(x^{\frac{1}{2}} - \frac{1}{2}\mathrm{e}^x)$ **5** $y = 4\ln x$ **6** $y = \frac{1}{3}\ln 9x$

7 $y = \ln x^4 - \ln x^{\frac{1}{3}}$ **8** $y = \log_5 x$

9 At the point A on the curve with equation $y = 2x^3 - 3\ln x$, $x = 1$. Find an equation of the normal to the curve at A.

10 Find the range of the function f, where

$$\mathrm{f}: x \mapsto 2x^3 - 54\ln x, \qquad x \in \mathbb{R}, x > 0$$

11 On the same axes sketch the curves with equations $y = \mathrm{e}^{x^2}$ and $y = -\mathrm{e}^{x^2}$.

State the equation of the tangent to each curve at the points where $x = 0$.

12 The tangent at the point where $x = k$ to the curve with equation $y = \mathrm{e}^x$ meets the x-axis at the point $(1, 0)$.

Find the value of k and the coordinates of the point where the tangent meets the y-axis.

13 Given that $y = Ax^2 - \mathrm{e}^x$, where A is a constant, prove that:

(a) $x\frac{\mathrm{d}y}{\mathrm{d}x} - 2y = (2 - x)\mathrm{e}^x$

(b) $x\frac{\mathrm{d}^2y}{\mathrm{d}x^2} - \frac{\mathrm{d}y}{\mathrm{d}x} = \mathrm{e}^x(1 - x)$

14 Given that $y = A\ln x$, where A is a constant, prove that:

(a) $\frac{\mathrm{d}y}{\mathrm{d}x}\ln x = \frac{y}{x}$

(b) $x\frac{\mathrm{d}^2y}{\mathrm{d}x} + \frac{\mathrm{d}y}{\mathrm{d}x} = 0$

15 Find the rate of change of y with respect to x at the point on the curve with equation $y = 10e^x - \frac{1}{2}x^2$ where $x = -1$.

16 Given that $y = 12 \ln x^2 - 6e^x - 5x^{\frac{3}{2}}$, find, to 3 significant figures, the values of $\frac{dy}{dx}$ and $\frac{d^2y}{dx^2}$ at the point where $x = \frac{1}{2}$.

Test yourself

Test yourself	What to review
	If your answer is incorrect:
1 Given that $y = -5e^x$, find $\frac{dy}{dx}$.	*Review Heinemann Book P2 pages 115–116*
2 Given that $y = \ln 6x$, find $\frac{dy}{dx}$.	*Review Heinemann Book P2 pages 116–119*
3 Find, in terms of e, the equation of the tangent and the equation of the normal to the curve with equation $y = 6e^x$ at the point where $x = \frac{1}{3}$.	*Review Heinemann Book P2 pages 119–123*
4 Given that $y = x^5 - 160 \ln x$, $x > 0$, find the minimum value of y to 3 significant figures.	*Review Heinemann Book P2 pages 116–119*

Test yourself answers

1 $-5e^x$ **2** $\frac{1}{x}$ **3** Tangent: $y - 6e^{\frac{1}{3}} = 6e^{\frac{1}{3}}(x - \frac{1}{3})$ Normal: $y - 6e^{\frac{1}{3}} = -\frac{1}{6e^{\frac{1}{3}}}(x - \frac{1}{3})$ **4** -78.9

Integration

7

Key points to remember

1 $\int e^x \, dx = e^x + C$

2 $\int ke^x \, dx = ke^x + C$, where k is a constant.

3 $\int \frac{1}{x} \, dx = \ln|x| + C$

4 $\int \frac{k}{x} \, dx = k \ln|x| + C$

5 The volume generated when R is rotated completely about the x-axis is

$$\pi \int_a^b y^2 \, dx = \pi \int_a^b [f(x)]^2 \, dx$$

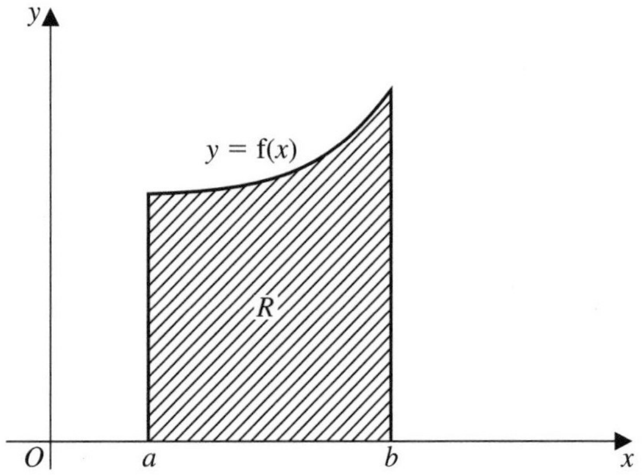

6 The volume generated when R is rotated completely about the y-axis is

$$\pi \int_p^q x^2 \, dy = \pi \int_p^q [g(y)]^2 \, dy$$

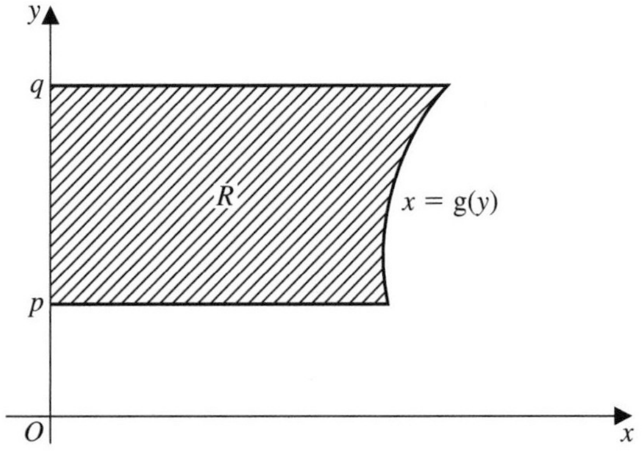

7

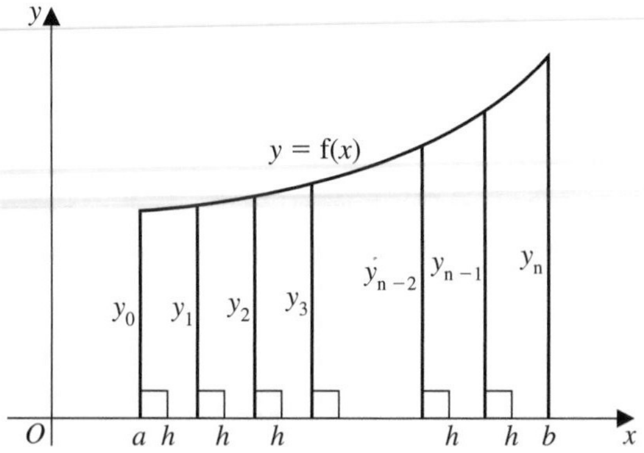

The trapezium rule states that the area of the region bounded by the curve with equation $y = \mathrm{f}(x)$, the x-axis and the ordinates $x = a$ and $x = b$ is approximately

$$\frac{h}{2}[y_0 + 2y_1 + 2y_2 + 2y_3 + \ldots + 2y_{n-2} + 2y_{n-1} + y_n],$$

where $h = \dfrac{b-a}{n}$.

Example 1

Integrate with respect to x:

(a) $\frac{1}{4}\mathrm{e}^x$

(b) $\left(3x + \dfrac{2}{x^2}\right)^2$

Answer

(a) $\displaystyle\int \tfrac{1}{4}\mathrm{e}^x\,\mathrm{d}x$

$= \tfrac{1}{4}\displaystyle\int \mathrm{e}^x\,\mathrm{d}x$ — Using **1**

$= \tfrac{1}{4}\mathrm{e}^x + C$

(b) $\left(3x + \dfrac{2}{x^2}\right)^2 = 9x^2 + \dfrac{12}{x} + \dfrac{4}{x^4}$

$= 9x^2 + \dfrac{12}{x} + 4x^{-4}$

So $\displaystyle\int \left(3x + \frac{2}{x^2}\right)^2 \mathrm{d}x = \int \left(9x^2 + \frac{12}{x} + 4x^{-4}\right) \mathrm{d}x$

$= 3x^3 + 12\ln|x| - \tfrac{4}{3}x^{-3} + C$ — Using **4**

$= 3x^3 + 12\ln|x| - \dfrac{4}{3x^3} + C$

Example 2

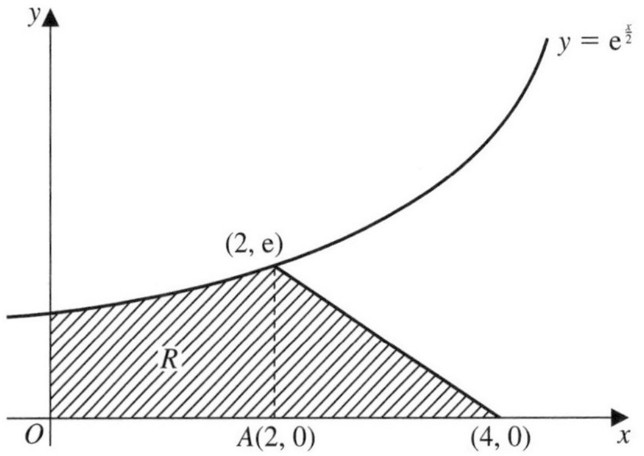

The diagram shows the finite region R, bounded by the curve with equation $y = e^{\frac{x}{2}}$, the x-axis, the y-axis and the line joining the points (2, e) and (4, 0).

The region R is rotated completely about the x-axis. Find the volume of the solid so formed.

Answer

The part of the region to the left of the line joining (2, e) and (2, 0), when rotated, has volume

$$\pi \int_0^2 (e^{\frac{x}{2}})^2 \, dx = \pi \int_0^2 e^x \, dx$$

Using **5**

$$= \pi \left[e^x \right]_0^2$$

Using **1**

$$= \pi[e^2 - e^0]$$

$$= \pi[e^2 - 1]$$

The volume of the triangular region when rotated is

$$\tfrac{1}{3}\pi e^2 \times 2 = \tfrac{2}{3}\pi e^2$$

Using volume of a cone $= \frac{1}{3}\pi r^2 h$

Total volume is $\pi e^2 - \pi + \frac{2}{3}\pi e^2$

$$= \pi[\tfrac{5}{3}e^2 - 1]$$

Example 3

Two variables x and y are related by the differential equation

$$x \frac{dy}{dx} = 4xe^x - 3$$

At $x = 1$, $y = 5$.
Find the value of y at $x = 3$.

Answer

$$x\frac{dy}{dx} = 4xe^x - 3$$

$$\frac{dy}{dx} = 4e^x - \frac{3}{x}$$

$$\text{So } y = \int\left(4e^x - \frac{3}{x}\right) dx$$

$$= 4e^x - 3\ln|x| + C$$

Using 2 and 4

At $x = 1$, $y = 5$

so $5 = 4e - 3\ln 1 + C$

$\Rightarrow$ $5 = 4e - 0 + C$

Using $\ln 1 = 0$

$\Rightarrow$ $C = 5 - 4e$

Thus $y = 4e^x - 3\ln|x| + 5 - 4e$

At $x = 3$

$$y = 4e^3 - 3\ln|3| + 5 - 4e$$

$$= 4e^3 - 3\ln 3 + 5 - 4e$$

Example 4

Find, in terms of e, an estimate of $\int_0^2 e^x\,dx$ by using the trapezium rule with 3 equally spaced ordinates.

Answer

Let $y = e^x$

x	0	1	2
y	1	e	e^2

By the trapezium rule

$$\int_0^2 e^x\,dx \approx \tfrac{1}{2}[1 + 2e + e^2]$$

$$= \tfrac{1}{2}(1 + e)^2$$

Using 7 with $h = 1$

Revision exercise 7

In questions 1–5 integrate with respect to x.

1 $\frac{1}{7}e^x$ **2** $-\frac{5}{x}$ **3** $3(x - x^{-1})$

4 $2x^{-1} - \frac{1}{3}e^x$ **5** $\frac{1}{3}e^x - 9x^{-1} + \frac{1}{3}x^3$

In questions 6–8 evaluate the integrals.

6 $\int_{-1}^{2} (e^x - \frac{1}{2}x)\,dx$ **7** $\int_3^5 \left(6 - \frac{4}{x}\right) dx$ **8** $\int_1^2 \left(x - \frac{1}{x}\right)^3 dx$

9 $\frac{dy}{dx}$ is directly proportional to e^x, $y = 1$ at $x = 1$ and $y = 2$ at $x = 0$.

Find the value of y when $x = -1$.

10 The diagram shows the region R bounded by the line $y = 5$, the y-axis and the curve with equation $y^2 = x$.

(a) Find the area of R.

(b) Find the volume generated when R is rotated completely about the y-axis.

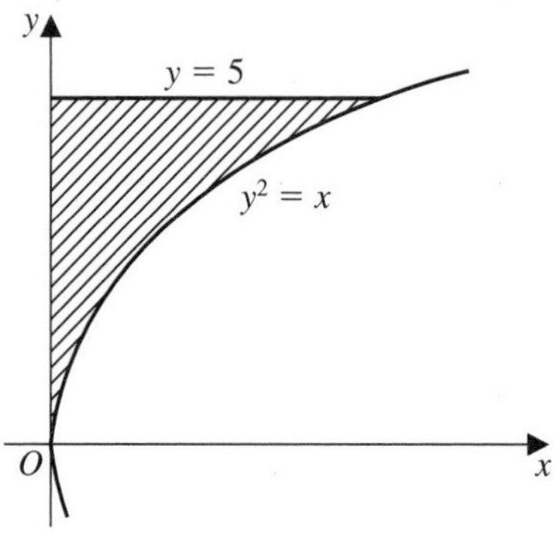

11 The region bounded by the y-axis, the lines $y = 1$, $y = 3$ and the curve with equation $y = \ln x^2$ is rotated completely about the y-axis.

Find the volume so generated.

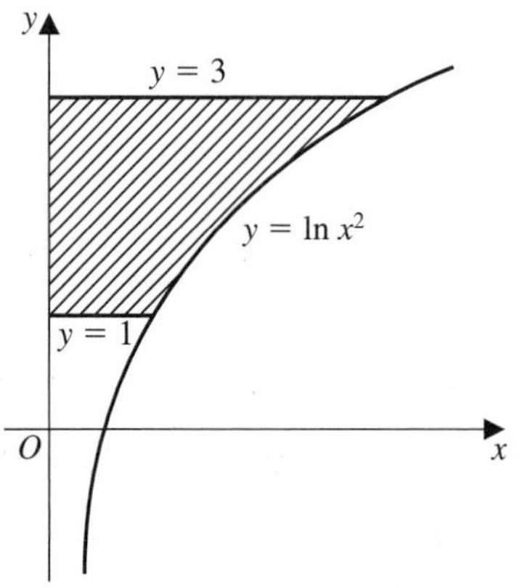

12 Use the trapezium rule with 5 strips of equal width to find an estimate of the area of the region given in question 11.

13

x	0	$\frac{\pi}{12}$	$\frac{\pi}{6}$	$\frac{\pi}{4}$	$\frac{\pi}{3}$
$\tan x^2$	0	0.0686	0.2812	0.7092	1.9485

The table gives 4 values of x and the corresponding values of $\tan x^2$ to 4 decimal places. Use the trapezium rule with 5 ordinates and only the values in the table to estimate to 2 decimal places the value of

$$\int_0^{\frac{\pi}{3}} \tan x^2 \, dx$$

Test yourself	What to review
	If your answer is incorrect:
1 Find $\int -6e^x \, dx$	*Review Heinemann Book P2 pages 125–126*
2 Evaluate $\int_1^3 (\frac{1}{3} e^x - 5) \, dx$	*Review Heinemann Book P2 pages 125–126*
3 Given that $\frac{dy}{dx} = 2e^x - \frac{4}{3x}$ and $y = 0$ at $x = 1$, find y in terms of x for $x > 0$.	*Review Heinemann Book P2 pages 125–129*
4 (see below)	*Review Heinemann Book P2 pages 132–136*
5 (a) Use the trapezium rule with 3 equally spaced ordinates to find an estimate of the area of the region bounded by the lines $x = \pm\frac{1}{5}$, the x-axis and the curve with equation $y = e^x$.	*Review Heinemann Book P2 pages 137–141*

4

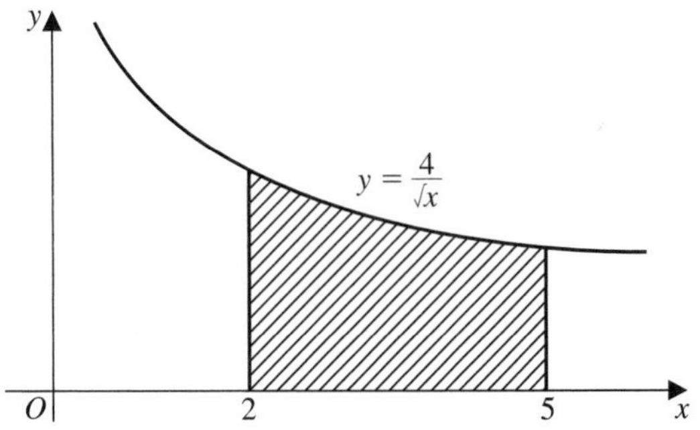

Find, in terms of π, the volume generated when the region bounded by the curve with equation $y = \frac{4}{\sqrt{x}}$, the x-axis and the lines $x = 2$ and $x = 5$ is rotated completely about the x-axis.

5 (a) Use the trapezium rule with 3 equally spaced ordinates to find an estimate of the area of the region bounded by the lines $x = \pm\frac{1}{5}$, the x-axis and the curve with equation $y = e^x$.

(b) By integration, evaluate the exact area and hence find, to 2 decimal places, the percentage error incurred by using the trapezium rule with 3 equally spaced ordinates.

Test yourself answers

1 $-6e^x + C$ **2** $\frac{1}{3}e^3 - \frac{1}{3}e - 10$ **3** $y = 2e^x - 2e - \frac{4}{3}\ln x$ **4** $16\pi \ln \frac{5}{2}$ **5 (a)** 0.4040 **(b)** $e^{0.2} - e^{-0.2}$, 0.33%

Numerical methods

8

Key points to remember

1 If $f(x_1) > 0$ and $f(x_2) < 0$ or if $f(x_1) < 0$ and $f(x_2) > 0$ and if f is continuous in the interval between x_1 and x_2, then the equation $f(x) = 0$ has a root in the interval $[x_1, x_2]$.

2 In order to find a root of the equation $f(x) = 0$ by iteration, rearrange the equation into the form $x = g(x)$ and then an iteration formula is $x_{n+1} = g(x_n)$.

3 Each iteration formula with a given starting point leads to one root of the equation at most.

4 Sometimes an iteration formula with a given starting point does not lead to a root of the equation.

Example 1

$f(x) \equiv \cos x - 7x$

(a) Show that a root α of the equation $f(x) = 0$ lies in the interval $[0.11, 0.15]$.

(b) Investigate further to determine whether or not the value of α is 0.14 correct to 2 decimal places.

Answer

(a) $f(0.11) = \cos 0.11 - 0.77 = 0.224$

$f(0.15) = \cos 0.15 - 1.05 = -0.061$

Since $f(0.11) > 0$ and $f(0.15) < 0$ and f is continuous there is a root α of $f(x) = 0$ which lies in the interval $[0.11, 0.15]$.

Using **1**

(b) Everything in the interval $[0.135, 0.145)$ rounds to 0.14 (to 2 d.p.).

Now $f(0.135) = 0.046$ (3 d.p.)

and $f(0.145) = -0.025$ (3 d.p.)

The sign change indicates that α lies in the interval $[0.135, 0.145)$.

Using **1**

So $\alpha = 0.14$ (correct to 2 d.p.)

Example 2

Given that the equation $x^5 - 80x + 4 = 0$ has exactly 3 real roots and each root lies in the interval $(N, N + 1)$ where $N \in \mathbb{Z}$, find the possible values of N.

Answer

Let $f(x) = x^5 - 80x + 4$.
$f(-4) = -1024 + 320 + 4 = -700 < 0$
$f(-3) = -243 + 240 + 4 = +1 > 0$
Since $f(-4) < 0$ and $f(-3) > 0$ there is a root of $f(x) = 0$ in the interval $[-4, -3]$. Using **1**

$f(0) = 4 > 0$
$f(1) = 1 - 80 + 4 = -75 < 0$

Since $f(0) > 0$ and $f(1) < 0$ and f is continuous, there is a root of $f(x) = 0$ in the interval $[0, 1]$. Using **1**

$f(2) = 32 - 160 + 4 = -124 < 0$
$f(3) = 243 - 240 + 4 = 7 > 0$

Since $f(2) < 0$ and $f(3) > 0$ and f is continuous, there is a root of $f(x) = 0$ in the interval $[2, 3]$. Using **1**
So the possible values of N are -4, 0 and 2.

Example 3

(a) By considering sketch graphs of the line $y = 5 - x$ and the curve with equation $y = e^x$, show that the equation $x + e^x - 5 = 0$ has just one root α.
(b) Show that $x_{n+1} = \ln(5 - x_n)$, might be an appropriate iteration formula to use to find α, using a starting point $x_0 = 2$.
(c) Hence find α to 2 decimal places.

Answer

(a)

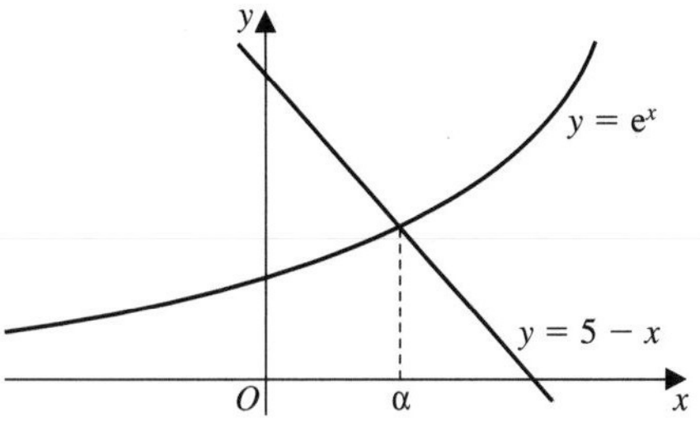

From the sketch graphs, it is clear that the line and the curve only intersect once. Hence the equation $x + e^x - 5 = 0$, which can be written $5 - x = e^x$, has only one root.

(b) $f(x) = x + e^x - 5 = 0$
can be rewritten

$$5 - x = e^x$$

So $\quad \ln(5 - x) = \ln e^x$
$\Rightarrow \quad \ln(5 - x) = x \ln e$
$\Rightarrow \quad \ln(5 - x) = x$ Using **2**

So $x_{n+1} = \ln(5 - x_n)$ is a possible iteration formula for finding the root α.

Since $f(1) = 1 + e - 5 = e - 4 < 0$
and $f(2) = 2 + e^2 - 5 = e^2 - 3 > 0$
and f is continuous, α lies in the interval [1, 2].
Hence $x_0 = 2$ could be an appropriate starting point for the iteration procedure.

Using **1**

(c) Working to 4 decimal places with $x_0 = 2$ and $x_{n+1} = \ln(5 - x_n)$,

$x_1 = 1.0986$ $x_5 = 1.3055$
$x_2 = 1.3613$ $x_6 = 1.3069$
$x_3 = 1.2916$ $x_7 = 1.3065$
$x_4 = 1.3106$ $x_8 = 1.3066$

Since x_5, x_6, x_7, x_8 all round to 1.31 (2 d.p.), this is a possible value of α.

Everything in the interval [1.305, 1.315) rounds to 1.31.

$f(1.305) = -0.007\,31 < 0$
$f(1.315) = 0.039\,75 > 0$

Since $f(1.305) < 0$ and $f(1.315) > 0$ and f is continuous, α lies in [1.305, 1.315) and so $\alpha = 1.31$ (correct to 2 d.p.)

Using **1**

Example 4

(a) Show that the equation $f(x) \equiv x^4 - 5x + 2 = 0$ has a root in the interval [1.5, 1.6].
(b) Use the iterative formula $x_{n+1} = (5x_n - 2)^{\frac{1}{4}}$, $x_0 = 1.6$, to find the root α correct to 3 decimal places.

Answer

(a) $f(1.5) = 1.5^4 - (5 \times 1.5) + 2 = -0.4375$
$f(1.6) = 1.6^4 - (5 \times 1.6) + 2 = 0.5536$

So $f(1.5) < 0$ and $f(1.6) > 0$ and since f is continuous on the interval [1.5, 1.6], $f(x) = 0$ has a root in [1.5, 1.6].

Using **1**

(b) Using $x_{n+1} = (5x_n - 2)^{\frac{1}{4}}$ with $x_0 = 1.6$,

$x_1 = 1.5651$ $x_4 = 1.5484$
$x_2 = 1.5536$ $x_5 = 1.5480$
$x_3 = 1.5497$ $x_6 = 1.5478$

It therefore appears that $\alpha = 1.548$ to 3 decimal places.

Consider the interval [1.5475, 1.5485].
Everything in the interval rounds to 1.548 to 3 d.p.

Now $f(1.5475) = -2.64 \times 10^{-3}$
and $f(1.5485) = 7.20 \times 10^{-3}$.
So $f(1.5475) < 0$ and $f(1.5485) > 0$
and f is continuous in [1.5475, 1.5485] so α lies in [1.5475, 1.5485).
Hence $\alpha = 1.548$ correct to 3 decimal places.

Using **1**

Revision exercise 8

1 Show that the equation $\cot x = \ln x$ has a root in the interval $[1.3, 1.4]$.

2 Show that the equation $\ln x = \sin x$ has a root whose value is 2.22 correct to 2 decimal places.

3 The roots of the equation $x^3 - 21x^2 + 35x - 7 = 0$ are real, distinct and positive. Find intervals in the form $[N, N + 1]$, where N is an integer, in which each root lies.

4 $\quad f(x) \equiv e^x - x^2 - 2$

Prove that the equation $f(x) = 0$ has a root α in the interval $[1, 2]$.
Use the iterative formula $x_{n+1} = \ln(x_n^2 + 2)$, $x_0 = 1.4$, to find α correct to 3 significant figures.

5 Prove that the equation $\sin x = \dfrac{3 - 2x}{2(1 + \cos x)}$ has a root α in the interval $[0.5, 0.6]$.

Use the iteration formula $x_{n+1} = \arcsin\left[\dfrac{3 - 2x_n}{2(1 + \cos x_n)}\right]$ with $x_0 = 0.5$ to obtain x_1, x_2, x_3 and x_4 each to 4 decimal places.
Show that, when rounded to 2 d.p., the value of x_4 gives α correct to 2 d.p.

6 Show that the curve with equation $y = x^4 + 7x - 19$ has just one turning point and determine the x-coordinate of the turning point.
Show further that the equation $x^4 + 7x - 19 = 0$ has two real roots, one in $[-3, -2]$ and one in $[1, 2]$.
Sketch the graph of the curve with equation $y = x^4 + 7x - 19$.

7 $\quad f(x) \equiv x^3 + 3x - 15$

(a) Show that the equation $f(x) = 0$ can be written as

$$x = (15 - 3x)^{\frac{1}{3}}$$

(b) Use the iterative formula

$$x_{n+1} = (15 - 3x_n)^{\frac{1}{3}}, \ x_0 = 2.1$$

to determine the real root of the equation $f(x) = 0$ correct to 3 decimal places.

Test yourself

What to review

If your answer is incorrect:

1 (a) Prove that the equation $x^2 - 121x + 100 = 0$ has a root in the interval [120, 121].
(b) A second root of the equation lies in the interval $[N, N + 1]$, where N is an integer. Find the value of N.

Review Heinemann Book P2 pages 143–147

---

2 (a) Prove that the equation $2x - \tan x = 0$ has a root α in the interval [1.1, 1.2].
(b) Prove further that $\alpha = 1.17$ correct to 2 decimal places.
(c) Show that $-\alpha$ is also a root of the equation.

Review Heinemann Book P2 pages 143–147 and 155–159.

---

3 (a) Prove that the equation $f(x) \equiv x \sec x - 3 = 0$ has a root in the interval [1.1, 1.2].
(b) By using the iterative formula $x_{n+1} = \arccos \frac{x_n}{3}$, $x_0 = 1.2$, find α correct to 3 decimal places.

Review Heinemann Book P2 pages 143–159

Test yourself answers

1 (a) Let $f(x) = x^2 - 121x + 100$
$f(120) = -20$
$f(121) = 100$
Since f is continuous on [120, 121], $f(120) < 0$ and $f(121) > 0$, $f(x) = 0$ has a root in [120, 121].
(b) 0

2 (a) Let $f(x) = 2x - \tan x$
$f(1.1) = 0.2352\ldots$
$f(1.2) = -0.1721\ldots$
Since f is continuous on [1.1, 1.2], $f(1.1) > 0$ and $f(1.2) < 0$, a root α lies in [1.1, 1.2].
(b) Everything in the interval [1.165, 1.175) rounds to 1.17 to 2 d.p.
$f(1.165) = 0.002\,48\ldots$
$f(1.175) = -0.043\,22\ldots$
Since f is continuous in [1.165, 1.175), $f(1.165) > 0$ and $f(1.175) < 0$, α lies in [1.165, 1.175) and so $\alpha = 1.17$ correct to 2 d.p.
(c) f is an odd function so it follows that
$f(-\alpha) = 2(-\alpha) - \tan(-\alpha) = -f(\alpha)$
and $-2\alpha + \tan\alpha = 0$
So $-\alpha$ is a root of the equation $f(x) = 0$.

3 (a) $f(1.1) = -0.5749\ldots$
$f(1.2) = 0.3116\ldots$
Since f is continuous on [1.1, 1.2], $f(1.1) < 0$ and $f(1.2) > 0$, $f(x) = 0$ has a root in [1.1, 1.2]
(b) 1.170

Proof

9

Key points to remember

1 For a direct proof you start with what you know and proceed through a number of logical steps to the conclusion required.

2 If an assertion or proposition is suspected of being false, then one single counter-example is sufficient to prove the assertion false.

3 In some circumstances it is possible to prove that an assertion is true by assuming first that it is false, and showing that this assumption leads to a contradiction.

Example 1

Given that

$$x = a\sec\theta + b\tan\theta,$$
$$y = a\sec\theta - b\tan\theta,$$

prove that

$$b^2(x+y)^2 - a^2(x-y)^2 = 4a^2b^2$$

Answer

$$x + y = 2a\sec\theta$$
$$x - y = 2b\tan\theta$$

So $b^2(x+y)^2 - a^2(x-y)^2$

$$= b^2(4a^2\sec^2\theta) - a^2(4b^2\tan^2\theta)$$
$$= 4a^2b^2\sec^2\theta - 4a^2b^2\tan^2\theta$$
$$= 4a^2b^2(\sec^2\theta - \tan^2\theta)$$
$$= 4a^2b^2, \text{ as required}$$

Using $1 + \tan^2\theta \equiv \sec^2\theta$ and **1**

Example 2

The positive numbers p, q and r, where $p < q < r$, are 3 consecutive terms of a geometric series.
Prove that $\ln p$, $\ln q$ and $\ln r$ are 3 consecutive terms of an arithmetic series.

Answer

Since p, q and r are 3 consecutive terms of a geometric series

$$\frac{r}{q} = \frac{q}{p}$$

$$\Rightarrow \quad pr = q^2$$

Using definition of a geometric series.

So $\quad \ln(pr) = \ln(q^2)$

$\Rightarrow \quad \ln p + \ln r = 2\ln q$

$\Rightarrow \quad \ln r - \ln q = \ln q - \ln p$

Using laws of logarithms.

But if this is the case then $\ln p$, $\ln q$ and $\ln r$ are 3 consecutive terms of an arithmetic series, as required.

Using definition of an arithmetic series and **1**.

Example 3

It is asserted that

$$\sum_{r=1}^{n} r = \tfrac{1}{12}(n^3 + 17n - 6)$$

is true for all $n \in \mathbb{Z}^+$.

Disprove the assertion by counter-example.

Answer

$n = 1$, $\frac{1}{12}(1^3 + 17 - 6) = 1$, which is true.

$n = 2$, $\frac{1}{12}[2^3 + 34 - 6) = 3 = 1 + 2$, which is true.

$n = 3$, $\frac{1}{12}[3^3 + 51 - 6] = 6 = 1 + 2 + 3$, which is true.

$n = 4$, $\frac{1}{12}[4^3 + 68 - 6] = 10.5 \neq 1 + 2 + 3 + 4$

Since the assertion is not true for $n = 4$, the assertion is not true for all $n \in \mathbb{Z}^+$.

Using **2**

Example 4

Prove, by contradiction, that $x^n - 1$, where n is a positive integer, is divisible by $x - 1$.

Answer

Assume that $(x^n - 1)$ is not divisible by $x - 1$. Then when $(x^n - 1)$ is divided by $(x - 1)$ there is a remainder.

Using **3**

So if $f(x) \equiv x^n - 1$, then the assumption is

$$f(x) \equiv (x - 1)g(x) + R$$

where g is a polynomial of degree $(n - 1)$ and R is the remainder.

Now $f(1) = 1^n - 1 = 1 - 1 = 0$

But $\quad f(1) = (1 - 1)g(1) + R$

$\quad = 0 \times g(1) + R$

$\quad = R$

This is a contradiction.

So the assumption is false and hence $(x^n - 1)$ is divisible by $(x - 1)$.

Revision exercise 9

1 Given that $\tan\frac{x}{2} = t$, prove that

$$\cos x = \frac{1-t^2}{1+t^2}$$

2 The equation $x^3 - 3x^2 - 2x + 3 = 0$ has a root in the interval $[N, N+1]$, where N is an integer.
Prove that there are three possible values of N and find these values.

3 Prove that the equation $x^3 + 3x - 5 = 0$ has just one real root and that it lies in the interval [1, 2].

4 The function f is given by
$$\mathrm{f}: x \mapsto x^2 + 2x + 5, \qquad x \in \mathbb{R}$$
Prove that:
(a) $\mathrm{f}(x) > 0$
(b) the line with equation $y = \frac{1}{2}x + 6$ is a normal to the curve with equation $y = x^2 + 2x + 5$.

5 Given that A and B are two angles in a triangle, prove that:
(a) $A > B \Rightarrow \cos A < \cos B$
(b) $\sin A = \sin B \Rightarrow A = B$
(c) $A < B \Rightarrow \sin A < \sin B$

6 Prove that the equation
$$(x+2)^4 - (x-2)^4 = 80$$
can be reduced to the equation
$$x^3 + 4x - 5 = 0$$
Hence prove that the equation has only one real root.

7 Prove that the coefficient of x^3 in the expansion of $(1 + x + x^2)^n$, where n is a positive integer, is $\frac{1}{6}n(n-1)(n+4)$.

8 Given that $\ln(x - y) = \frac{1}{2}(\ln x + \ln y)$, prove that
$$2\ln(x+y) = \ln x + \ln y + \ln 5$$

9 The one–one functions f and g are defined for $x \in \mathbb{R}$. The following three assertions are made concerning f and g. Consider each one and if it is true, prove the assertion; on the other hand, if it is false provide a counter-example to disprove it.

(a) $\mathrm{f}^{-1} = \dfrac{1}{\mathrm{f}}$

(b) $(\mathrm{fg})^{-1} = \mathrm{f}^{-1}\mathrm{g}^{-1}$

(c) $\mathrm{ff}^{-1} : x \mapsto x$

10 For all real values of x, the following assertions are made about the function f, given by $\mathrm{f}(x) = x^2 + 2x + 5$.

(a) $\mathrm{f}(x) > 5$

(b) the minimum value of $\mathrm{f}(x)$ occurs at $x = -1$.

If an assertion is true, prove it. If an assertion is false, find a counter-example to disprove it.

11 Prove by contradiction that $\sqrt{2}$ is irrational.

12 Prove that the sequence of prime numbers is endless.

13 Prove that the squares of all odd positive integers are of the form $8n + 1$, where n is either zero or a positive integer.

14 Find a counter-example to disprove the statement:
For the continuous function f, $\mathrm{f}''(x) = 0$ at $x = a$ and it follows that the curve with equation $y = \mathrm{f}(x)$ has a point of inflexion at $x = a$.

15 Find a counter-example to disprove the statement:

$$x^3 = x \Rightarrow x = \pm 1 \text{ only.}$$

Give a reason to say whether, or not, the statement

$$x = \pm 1 \Rightarrow x^3 = x$$

is true.

16 Use a proof by contradiction to prove the statement

$$x^2 - 7x + 12 < 0 \Rightarrow 3 < x < 4$$

17 Find a counter-example to disprove the statement

$$0 < x < \frac{3\pi}{2} \Rightarrow \cos \tfrac{1}{2}x > \cos x$$

Test yourself | What to review

If your answer is incorrect:

1 Prove that

$$\int_2^4 \frac{1+3x^2}{x}\,dx = A + \ln 2$$

stating the value of the constant A.

Review Heinemann Book P1 pages 173–176

---

2 Prove that $\sum_{r=1}^{\infty} e^{-r} = \frac{1}{e-1}$

Review Heinemann Book P1 pages 173–176

---

3 $\quad f(x) \equiv x^2 + 2x + 5$

It is asserted that if $f(x) = 5$ then $x = 0$. Prove, by counter-example, that the assertion is false.

Review Heinemann Book P2 pages 162–164

---

4 Prove by contradiction that if N is an odd positive integer then N^2 is an odd positive integer.

Review Heinemann Book P2 pages 161–162

Test yourself answers

1 18

2 $\sum_{r=1}^{\infty} e^{-r} = \frac{1}{e} + \frac{1}{e^2} + \frac{1}{e^3} + \ldots$ This is a geometric series with first term $a = \frac{1}{e}$ and common ratio $r = \frac{1}{e}$ and $\left|\frac{1}{e}\right| < 1$.

The sum of an infinite geometric series with first term a and common ratio r is $\frac{a}{1-r}$

So $\quad \sum_{r=1}^{\infty} e^{-r} = \frac{\frac{1}{e}}{1-\frac{1}{e}}$

$$= \frac{\frac{1}{e}}{\frac{e-1}{e}}$$

$$= \frac{1}{e-1}, \text{ as required.}$$

3 $f(x) \equiv x^2 + 2x + 5$

$f(-2) = (-2)^2 + 2(-2) + 5$

$= 4 - 4 + 5$

$= 5$

So it is not true that if $f(x) = 5$ then x must equal 0.

4 Assume that N is an odd positive integer and that N^2 is an even positive integer.

Then $N = 2n - 1$, where n is a positive integer.

So $N^2 = (2n-1)^2 = 4n^2 - 4n + 1$

But $4n^2$ is even

and $4n$ is even

So $4n^2 - 4n + 1$ is odd

This is a contradiction.

So if N is an odd positive integer, then N^2 is an odd positive integer.

Examination style paper

Answer all questions. **Time allowed: 90 minutes**

1. Find, in surd form, the exact value of $\cos 75°$. **(3 marks)**

2. Given that $\dfrac{\ln p}{3} = \dfrac{\ln q}{5} = \ln x$, express:

(*a*) $\dfrac{q^2}{p^3}$ in terms of x

(*b*) $\ln p^3 - 2\ln q^2$ in terms of $\ln x$. **(5 marks)**

3. The number $N = n^2 + n + 11$, where n is a positive integer.
It is asserted that:
(*a*) N is always prime
(*b*) $\cos N\pi = \pm 1$
If an assertion is true, prove it. If an assertion is false, find a counter-example. **(5 marks)**

4. Given that the expansion of $(1 - 4x)^2(1 + kx)^8$ in ascending powers of x is $1 + 36x + Ax^2 + \ldots$, find the value of k and of A. **(6 marks)**

5. $f(x) \equiv \cos x - x^2, \quad x \in \mathbb{R}$

(*a*) Show that the equation $f(x) = 0$ has two real roots. **(3 marks)**

(*b*) Using the iterative relation

$$x_{n+1} = (\cos x_n)^{\frac{1}{2}}, \qquad x_0 = 0.8,$$

find the positive root correct to 3 decimal places. **(5 marks)**

6. $f(x) \equiv 9e^x - 4x^{\frac{2}{3}}, \quad x \in \mathbb{R}$

(*a*) Evaluate $\displaystyle\int_0^{\frac{1}{8}} f(x)\,dx$, giving your answer to 4 significant figures. **(5 marks)**

(*b*) The tangent at the point where $x = 1$ to the curve with equation $y = f(x)$ meets the x-axis at the point A. Find the distance between the origin O and A, giving your answer in terms of e. **(5 marks)**

7. (*a*) Prove that

$$\cos 5x + \cos x \equiv 2\cos 3x \cos 2x$$ **(3 marks)**

(*b*) Solve the equation $\cos 5x + \cos x = \cos 2x$, giving all answers in degrees in the interval $0 \leqslant x \leqslant 180°$. **(8 marks)**

8. The functions f and g are defined for all real values of x by

$$\mathrm{f}: x \mapsto x^2$$

$$\mathrm{g}: x \mapsto 21 - 4x$$

(*a*) Express the composite function gf in terms of x and find its range. **(5 marks)**

(*b*) Find the value of x for which

$$\mathrm{gg}(x) = \mathrm{g}^{-1}(x)$$ **(4 marks)**

(*c*) Solve the equation

$$\mathrm{f}(x) = |\mathrm{g}(x)|$$ **(4 marks)**

9. The curve C has equation $y = \dfrac{x+2}{x}, \qquad x > 0.$

(*a*) Find the gradient of C at the point on C where $x = \frac{1}{2}$. **(3 marks)**

(*b*) Hence find an equation of the normal to C at this point. **(3 marks)**

(*c*) Find the area of the finite region R bounded by C, the x-axis and the lines $x = \frac{1}{2}$ and $x = \frac{3}{2}$. **(3 marks)**

(*d*) Find the volume generated when the region R is rotated completely about the x-axis. **(5 marks)**

Answers

Revision exercise 1

1 $z = \dfrac{3xy}{y-2x}$ **2** $\dfrac{x+3}{x-1}$ **3** $\dfrac{x+1}{x+2}$

4 $\dfrac{y+1}{4y}$ **5** $\dfrac{2}{t(t+1)(t+2)}$

6 $\dfrac{1}{(x+1)(x+2)}$ **7** $\dfrac{3x+1}{(x-1)(x+1)}$

8 $\dfrac{2x+1}{x(x+1)}$ **9** $x = 2$ or 5

10 $x = 2$ or $-\frac{1}{2}$ **11** $x = 1$ or -2

12 $x = \frac{1}{2}$ or -2 **13** $(\frac{5}{2}, \frac{7}{4})$ or $(\frac{13}{24}, -\frac{13}{6})$

14 $x = 2$ or $-\frac{2}{3}$ **15** $x = 2.44$ or -1.44

Revision exercise 2

1 $f^{-1}(x) = \frac{1}{2}(x+5)$; $g^{-1}(x) = x^2 - 3, x > 0$;
$h^{-1}(x) = \dfrac{4-x}{x}, x \neq 0$

2 $fg(x) = 2\sqrt{(x+3)} - 5$; $fh(x) = \dfrac{3-5x}{x+1}, x \neq -1$
$hg(x) = \dfrac{4}{1+\sqrt{(x+3)}}$; $gf(x) = \sqrt{(2x-2)}$

3 $p = 19, q = 2$; Range of f is $\leqslant 19$

4 **(a)** Range of f is $\leqslant 16$
(b) $\pm 2\sqrt{5}, \pm 2\sqrt{3}$

6 $(-1, 2), (-\frac{1}{5}, \frac{2}{5})$ **7** $c = \dfrac{a}{2b}$

8 **(a)** $\dfrac{x-1}{x}$ **(b)** $\dfrac{2+x}{2-x}$ **(c)** $\dfrac{2}{1-x}$

9 **(a)** $gf: x \mapsto \dfrac{-3}{x+3}, \quad x \neq -3$
(b) $f^{-1}: x \mapsto 3x - 6, \quad x \in \mathbb{R}$

10 **(a)** $ff(x) = \dfrac{5x-2}{9-10x}, \quad x \neq \frac{9}{10}$
(b) $f^{-1}(x) = \dfrac{2x+1}{5x}, \quad x \neq 0$

11 $f: x \mapsto 3x$, $g: x \mapsto x^2$, $h: x \mapsto x - 2$;
$hgf: x \mapsto 9x^2 - 2$, $hfg: x \mapsto 3x^2 - 2$

12 $A(\frac{3}{2}, 0)$; $B(0, -9)$

13 **(a)** Range of f is $\frac{2}{3} \leqslant y \leqslant 2$

Revision exercise 3

1 **(a)** Diverges to $+\infty$
(b) Oscillates between 1 and -1
(c) Oscillates infinitely between $-\infty$ and $+\infty$ for large n
(d) Converges to 0 from above.

2 **(a)** $\frac{2}{3}, \frac{3}{4}, \frac{8}{11}$ **(b)** $\sqrt{3} - 1$

3 $n(n+2)$

4 **(a)** $10(1 - \frac{1}{2^n})$ **(b)** 10

5 0.000 04

6 **(a)** 3.1517 **(b)** 3

7 $1 - 6x + 15x^2 - 20x^3 + 15x^4 - 6x^5 + x^6$;
0.994 014 980 0

8 **(a)** $625 - 1000x + 600x^2 - 160x^3 + 16x^4$
(b) $-32x^5 + 400x^4 - 2000x^3 + 5000x^2 - 6250x + 3125$

9 $2 + 65x + 986x^2 + 9248x^3$

10 **(a)** $n = 7$ **(b)** $A = 2$; 280, 560

11 $1 - 15x^2 + 105x^4 - 455x^6$; 0.994 016 770 88

12 0.430 467 21

13 $n = 6$; 20, 6

Revision exercise 4

1 30°, 90°, 150°, 270°

2 60°, 150°

3 $-17 \leqslant f(x) \leqslant 17$

4 −105°, −15°

5 **(a)** $\frac{\pi}{8}, \frac{\pi}{4}, \frac{5\pi}{8}, \frac{9\pi}{8}, \frac{5\pi}{4}, \frac{13\pi}{8}$
(b) $\frac{\pi}{8}, \frac{3\pi}{8}, \frac{5\pi}{8}, \frac{7\pi}{8}, \frac{9\pi}{8}, \frac{11\pi}{8}, \frac{13\pi}{8}, \frac{15\pi}{8}$,
$\frac{\pi}{9}, \frac{5\pi}{9}, \frac{7\pi}{9}, \frac{11\pi}{9}, \frac{13\pi}{9}, \frac{17\pi}{9}$
(c) $\frac{\pi}{2}, \pi$

6 **(a)** $\pm\frac{1}{10}\sqrt{2}$ **(b)** $\pm\frac{7}{10}\sqrt{2}$

9 60°, 300°, 0, 180°, 360°

10 38.7°, 321.3°

11 28.1°, 121.9°, 208.1°, 301.9°

12 22.5°, 112.5°, 202.5°, 292.5°

13 0, 180°, 360°, 51.3°, 308.7°
14 10°, 40°, 130°, 190°, 220°, 310°
15 6.9°, 246.9°
16 67.4°, 0, 360°
17 3.53, 5.89
18 0, 3.14, 6.28, 0.96, 2.19, 4.10, 5.33
19 1.57
20 1.99, 5.86
21 1.74, 3.75
22 0, 3.14, 6.28, 1.45, 4.83
23 0.52, 2.62

Revision exercise 5

1 **(a)** $-3q$ **(b)** $q - p$
(c) $3p - 2q$ **(d)** $q + \frac{1}{2}p$
2 $m = 9, n = 5$
3 **(a)** -3.32 **(b)** ± 1.10
5 **(a)** $1, \frac{1}{9}$ **(b)** 1.46
(c) $f^{-1}: x \mapsto \log_3 x, x \in \mathbb{R}^+$
6 $\frac{1}{3}\log_2 x$, 4.76
7 $p = 4, q = 2$ or $p = 9, q = 3$
8 **(a)** Range y, where $y \in \mathbb{R}^+$
(b) $g^{-1}(x) = -\frac{1}{4}\ln x, x \in \mathbb{R}^+$
(c) 0.929
9 $-\ln 2, \ln 4$
10 $c = 4.19, k = 9.97$ each to 2 d.p.
11 **(a)** 6.38 (2 d.p.) **(b)** 65.84 (2 d.p.)
12 $x = \frac{1}{8}, y = \frac{1}{4}$
13 **(a)** $\frac{1}{2}$ **(b)** $1\frac{1}{2}$
14 1.09 (2 d.p.)
15 **(a)** 2

Revision exercise 6

1 $4e^x$ 2 $-\frac{1}{3}e^x$ 3 $6x - 7e^x$
4 $\frac{1}{4}(x^{-\frac{1}{2}} - e^x)$ 5 $\dfrac{4}{x}$ 6 $\dfrac{1}{3x}$
7 $\dfrac{4}{x} - \dfrac{1}{3x} = \dfrac{11}{3x}$ 8 $\dfrac{1}{x \ln 5}$
9 $y - 2 = -\frac{1}{3}(x - 1)$
10 Range is y where $y \geqslant 18(1 - \ln 9)$
11 $y = 1, y = -1$
12 $k = 2, (0, -e^2)$
15 $1 + 10e^{-1}$
16 $\dfrac{dy}{dx} = 32.8, \dfrac{d^2y}{dx^2} = -111$

Revision exercise 7

1 $\frac{1}{7}e^x + C$
2 $-5 \ln x + C$
3 $\frac{3}{2}x^2 - 3 \ln x + C$
4 $2 \ln x - \frac{1}{3}e^x + C$
5 $\frac{1}{3}e^x - 9 \ln x + \frac{1}{12}x^4 + C$
6 $e^2 - e^{-1} - \frac{3}{4}$
7 $12 - 4 \ln \frac{5}{3}$
8 $3 \ln 2 - \frac{9}{8}$
9 $2 + \dfrac{1}{e}$
10 **(a)** $\frac{125}{3}$ **(b)** 625π
11 $\pi e(e^2 - 1)$
12 5.70 units^2
13 0.53

Revision exercise 8

3 [0, 1], [1, 2], [19, 20]
4 1.32
5 0.5617, 0.5331, 0.5463, 0.5402
6 -1.205
7 **(b)** 2.065

Revision exercise 9

2 $-2, 0, 3$
9 **(a)** false **(b)** false **(c)** true
10 **(a)** false **(b)** true

Examination style paper

1 $\dfrac{\sqrt{3} - 1}{2\sqrt{2}}$
2 **(a)** x **(b)** $-11 \ln x$
3 **(a)** Not always prime – breaks down when $n = 10, \ldots$
(b) N is always odd because $n(n + 1)$ is necessarily even, so $n(n + 1) + 11$ is odd and $\cos N\pi$ for N odd is always either 1 or -1.
4 $k = \frac{11}{2}, A = 511$
5 **(b)** 0.824
6 **(a)** 1.123 **(b)** $\dfrac{4}{27e - 8}$
7 **(b)** 20°, 45°, 100°, 135°, 140°
8 **(a)** $gf(x) = 21 - 4x^2$; range $\leqslant 21$
(b) 4.2 **(c)** 3 or -7
9 **(a)** -8 **(b)** $16y - 2x = 79$
(c) $1 + 2 \ln 3$ **(d)** $\pi[\frac{19}{3} + 4 \ln 3]$